THE ASS(   :ATION

SAFEGUARDS IN THE SCHOOL LABORATORY

Prepared by

A Task Group of the Safeguards in Science Committee of the Association for Science Education

Tenth Edition
1996

SAFEGUARDS IN SCIENCE COMMITTEE

The Safeguards in Science Committee is a Service Group of the Association for Science Education (ASE), and is the successor to the Laboratory Safeguards Sub-committee. The full membership of the Committee at the time of the preparation of this edition is shown below. The writing was done by a Task Group, membership of which is indicated by *.

* Peter Borrows, Waltham Forest Evaluation & Advisory Service *(Chair)*
  John Carleton, Haberdashers' Aske's School, Elstree *(Secretary)*
* Phil Bunyan, Nottinghamshire Advisory & Inspection Service *(Task Group Secretary)*
* Ray Vincent, Ilford County High School
* 'Joe' Jefferies, King Edward VI School, Retford
* John Tranter, CLEAPSS School Science Service
  John Wray, consultant, formerly ILEA
* Des Dunne, Northamptonshire Inspection & Advisory Service
* Allen Cochrane, Scottish Schools Equipment Research Centre
* David Higgins, consultant, formerly Essex LEA
  John Lawrence, *(ASE Deputy Chief Executive)*

First edition 1947
(compiled by the Science Masters' Association and the Association of Women Science Teachers)

Second edition 1950

Third edition (revised and reset) 1957
Reprinted 1959

Fourth edition (revised and reset) 1961

Fifth edition (revised) 1965
Reprinted 1966, 1971

Sixth edition (revised and reset) 1972
Reprinted 1973 (twice)

Seventh edition (revised and reset) 1976

Eighth edition (revised and reset) 1981
Reprinted 1981

Ninth edition (revised and reset) 1988
Reprinted (with corrections) 1988

Tenth edition (revised and reset) 1996

Association for Science Education,
College Lane, Hatfield, Herts AL10 9AA
Telephone: 01707 267411 Fax: 01707 266532

© 1961, 1965, 1972, 1976, 1981, 1988, 1996
ISBN 0 86357 250 2   (John Murray ISBN: 0 7195 7374 2)

Contents

1 Introduction

1.1 Background

In the years since the previous edition of this booklet was published, all teachers have had to cope with a mass of educational legislation. Science teachers, in addition, have had to respond to an increasing number of statutory requirements in health and safety: the *COSHH Regulations*, the *Management of Health and Safety at Work Regulations*, and many others [see 2.2]. The concept of risk assessment has become common-place, increasing numbers of science departments have developed safety policies, and science staff have become much more aware of safety issues.

Despite anxieties engendered by the legislation, school science in practice is very safe. Evidence from accident statistics [see Ch. 4] suggests that a science laboratory is just about the safest place in any school. A representative of the Health and Safety Commission was quoted in 1995 as saying

> "... the number of laboratory accidents [is] vanishingly small when compared to accidents arising from trips, slips and falls ...".

In some ways, the greatest concern is over-reaction. It is an often-believed myth that many chemicals or procedures are banned whereas in practice such bans are very rare. However, pupils' education may suffer as a result of the misunderstanding.

The aim of this booklet is to offer an up-to-date account of the best advice available. Generally speaking, advice on particular hazards (Chapters 5-15) has not changed much since the 9th edition, although there are small but important changes in detail, and Chapter 15 (*Hazardous Chemicals*) has been re-structured. However, there have been major changes relating to the management of health and safety. As a result, we have substantially altered Chapters 2, 3 and 4. The original Chapter 16 has been removed (but most of its contents appear in appropriate places elsewhere) and the former Chapter 17 re-numbered accordingly. Most of the Appendices have also been removed, either to incorporate the subject matter into the main text, or because the level of detail is more appropriate in another publication and, for example, will appear in the next edition of *Topics in Safety*. A revised form of the Appendix on First Aid now appears in Chapter 17.

In 1978 the Association for Science Education (ASE) convened a meeting of a wide range of interested parties in an attempt to bring some order to apparent chaos and rationalize the welter of conflicting advice facing science teachers. As a result, several working parties were set up to try to find a consensus of opinion on various issues. Their reports initially appeared in *Education in Science* and were later reprinted as *Topics in Safety*. That process has continued: a 2nd edition of *Topics in Safety* appeared in 1988 and further articles have been published in *Education in Science* covering, for example, biotechnology and practical work with DNA. In addition, over the years many other safety articles have appeared in *School Science Review* and *Education in Science*. A collection of these has recently been reprinted by the ASE as *Safety Reprints*. Both *Safety Reprints* and *Topics in Safety* are complementary to this booklet.

The Association also publishes a leaflet for school and college governors on safety (one of a series of leaflets for governors) and a pamphlet for pupils: *Safety in the Lab*. At the time of writing, the Association is working on ideas for a more substantial pack of safety materials for pupils.

1.2 Scope of this Booklet

This booklet has been kept as brief as possible, in the hope that it will be read from cover to cover. It is important, for example, that physicists should read the section on chemicals, and that chemists and biologists should read the section on electrical hazards. For laboratory technicians or those new to, or returning to, teaching, the booklet will give an overview of the main safety problems in school science. For those with management responsibilities [see 3.1] it will serve as a reminder of the main issues they should be dealing with. Large type is used to emphasise the main principles, while a smaller type is used to give explanatory notes or to deal with problems which are of interest to a limited number of readers.

In this booklet we concentrate on the more common problems, the potentially serious ones, those where there has been a significant change of opinion in recent years, or those about which ASE members have expressed greatest concerns, as judged by their letters to Headquarters and to the Association's journals. *Safeguards in the School Laboratory* is intended to give an overview, alerting readers to problems, and there will often be a need to refer to more detailed sources of information. However we do go in to more detail on those areas where members have expressed particular concerns. In general, we have tried to interpret statutory requirements in the context of school science, rather than quoting directly from the legislation, although sometimes that is necessary.

The following abbreviations, which appear in the margin, have been used for the most commonly used references. We would recommend this as the minimum safety bibliography that any science department should possess.

Topics	*Topics in Safety*, ASE, 2nd edition, 1988, ISBN 0 86357 104 2 (3rd edition in preparation 1997)
Reprints	*Safety Reprints*, ASE, 1996, ISBN 0 86357 246 4
DfEE Safety	*Safety in Science Education*, DfEE, (1996, ISBN 0 11 270915 X)

Hazcards	*Hazcards*, CLEAPSS School Science Service, 1995
Handbook	*Laboratory Handbook*, CLEAPSS School Science Service, 1989 with additions dated 1991, 1992, 1994, 1995 and any later ones
SSERC	*Science and Technology Bulletin*, Scottish Schools Equipment Research Centre, quarterly publication
Haz Man	*Hazardous Chemicals Manual*, SSERC, (new edition in preparation 1995)
Microbiology	*Microbiology: an HMI Guide for Schools and FE*, HMSO, 1990, ISBN 0 11 270578 2

*Note that CLEAPSS[1] publications and the SSERC[2] *Bulletin* are available only to schools, colleges or education authorities which are subscribers. Generally speaking, where both SSERC and CLEAPSS references occur, readers would only need to refer to one or the other.

In addition to the above publications which are referred to frequently, there are also references to *Administrative Memoranda* (AM) and other publications from the Department for Education and Employment (DfEE), formerly the Department of Education and Science (DES) and the Department for Education (DfE). The Department is referred to by the abbreviation current at the time of the original publication. For readers in Scotland there are references to the equivalent Scottish Office Education Department (SOED) *Circulars*, and to comparable publications of the Welsh Office (WO) and Department of Education for Northern Ireland (DENI). Schools in Northern Ireland should pay particular attention to the guidance in *Safety in Science Laboratories*.[3]

Safeguards in the School Laboratory is intended for teachers and technicians working with pupils and students of secondary school age (ie up to GCE or GNVQ advanced level), whether in secondary schools or colleges, or, in appropriate cases, middle and special schools. A characteristic of such institutions is that teaching is largely carried out in specialist accommodation. A companion publication, *Be safe! Some aspects of safety in school science and technology for key stages 1 and 2* (ASE, 2nd edition, 1990), gives similar guidance for those teaching in primary schools, where there is generally no specialist accommodation. A Scottish edition of *Be safe!* was published in 1995.

Much of the advice will also be applicable outside the UK, especially where it refers to the hazards of particular practical activities. The legislative framework governing health and safety practices will obviously differ. However, within the European Union, EU Directives are applicable in all

---

[1] CLEAPSS School Science Service, at Brunel University, Uxbridge, UB8 3PH.
   Telephone: 01895 251496, Fax: 01895 814372
[2] Scottish Schools Equipment Research Centre, 24 Bernard Terrace, Edinburgh, EH8 9NX
   Telephone 0131 668 4421, Fax: 0131 667 9344
[3] *Safety in Science Laboratories*, DENI Safety Series No. 1 (1989)

member states, although the mechanism for their implementation may differ in detail.

Many education employers [see 3.2] have adopted previous editions of this booklet as part of their safety advice to schools (for example, issuing copies to all newly qualified science teachers) and, it is hoped, will wish to do so for this edition. However, readers are reminded that whatever is written here, teachers and technicians must obey any local rules or guidance issued by their employers. In addition, they should keep abreast of developments in laboratory safety, for example, by reading the relevant columns of *School Science Review* and *Education in Science*.

1.3   Acknowledgements

In compiling this edition, as with its predecessors, we have been much helped in identifying the main issues by science teachers who have written to ASE headquarters, asking for advice or reporting accidents, incidents and "near-misses". It is hoped that teachers will continue to keep in touch with the Association about safety problems, whether they arise from particular practical activities, or more generally from the management of safety in schools. We would also like to hear of suggestions for safer alternatives to traditional practical activities.

The Task Group responsible for writing this edition would like to acknowledge the valuable help received with this and earlier editions from a large number of individuals and organisations, particularly past and present members of the Safeguards in Science Committee (and its predecessor, the Laboratory Safeguards Sub-committee), the Health and Safety Executive, the CLEAPSS School Science Service, the Scottish Schools Equipment Research Centre (SSERC), Science Advisers/Inspectors and Advisory Teachers and HM Inspectors of Schools (Ofsted). Finally, we should like to record our debt to the late Mr H G Andrew, a member of the Committee for some 40 years, its Chair for 30, and an active contributor to the first eight editions of this booklet.

1.4   Insurance

Members' attention is drawn to the fact that the Association for Science Education has arranged an insurance scheme with Commercial Union as an automatic privilege of membership.

This insurance assists individual members (whether teachers or technicians) in the UK with any civil action taken against them in the courts for the death of, or injury to, any person and indemnifies against loss of, or damage to, property either happening, or caused, during the performance of members' professional duties. (This only covers teachers in primary schools if they are individual members of the Association, rather than as part of a collective school membership.) In the case of a teacher or technician prosecuted under the *Health and Safety at Work Act* it would pay for legal costs, but not for any fines imposed. Further information is available from ASE Headquarters, College Lane, Hatfield, Herts AL10 9AA. (Telephone: 01707 267411, Fax: 01707 266532).

1.5   In-service Training

In addition to publishing booklets such as this and safety articles in its journals, the Association for Science Education also organises in-service training on safety for its members.

> This sometimes takes the form of lectures or seminars at the Association's Annual Meeting in early January, or at Regional Conferences or local meetings. In addition, the Safeguards in Science Committee has developed *Management of Safety: a Course for Heads of Science*, which is delivered around the country from time to time, and the course can, on request, be held at any venue, or be adapted to cater for the whole science department of a particular school. To discuss possibilities, or find out the date of the next course in your area, please contact ASE INSET Services, Barclay's Venture Centre, University of Warwick Science Park, Sir William Lyons Road, Coventry CV4 7EZ. (Telephone: 01203 690053; Fax: 01203 690726.)
>
> A *Science Technicians' Safety Course* has also been developed with sponsorship from Esso, and is being piloted at the time of writing. It should be fully available from 1996. Please contact ASE INSET Services (details as in the previous paragraph) for the latest information about availability in your area.
>
> For primary school teachers, the Association publishes *Safety in Science for Primary Schools: an INSET Pack* (ASE, 1994). Copies can be obtained from ASE Publications Department, Hatfield.

In addition to ASE, other organisations and individuals also run INSET on safety in school science. Some courses, provided by those with a good understanding of both health and safety and school science (such as CLEAPSS and SSERC [see 1.2]), are excellent. However, members are advised to be cautious when purchasing INSET from safety consultants and to ensure that such "experts" *do* understand the particular issues relating to school science and the curriculum, and do not try to apply industrial principles unthinkingly.

2 Health and Safety Legislation

2.1 The Health and Safety at Work Act

DfEE Safety Ch. 2

A major intention of the *Health and Safety at Work etc Act (HSW Act)* is to protect employees (ie, in science departments – teachers and technicians) and, to this end, employers are required to provide safe working conditions, information and training for health and safety, and a safety policy. The health and safety of the public at large, including pupils and students, must also be ensured, as far as is reasonably practicable. Manufacturers and suppliers must ensure that the equipment and materials they sell will not endanger the health and safety of the user and they are obliged to provide information about the hazards of their products.[1]

Handbook Ch.2.1

Employees have a duty to take reasonable care for the health and safety of themselves and others, and to cooperate with their employers in matters relating to health and safety.

Since its principal purpose is the protection of employees, the main duties of the Act are placed on employers: in schools and colleges this could be the education authority, board of governors, trust or, occasionally, an individual. Such employers are, for example, required to provide all necessary protective equipment for their employees, ie, teachers and technicians. Employers' obligations in this respect do **not** extend to pupils but they do indicate appropriate standards for satisfying the more general duty of care for non-employees required by the Act.

DfEE Safety Ch.2.1

An employer can delegate functions to teachers and technicians, ie, to carry out certain tasks, including those relating to health and safety. In accepting such functions, employees do **not** become responsible in the event of an accident, unless, for example, gross negligence or disregard for an employer's instructions could be demonstrated. The employer would

Handbook Ch.2.1.3

still be held responsible, perhaps by having failed to train the employee adequately or by not providing sufficient resources (time and money) for the employee to carry out the tasks adequately.

---

[1] 'From instinct to statute', *Phys. Educ.*, 1991, 26.

Reprints
Sec.A

The *HSW Act* makes neglect of safety precautions a criminal offence, when the state can prosecute. However, there have been **only two** such successful prosecutions of science teachers under the *HSW Act* since it was introduced in 1975. In both 1986 and 1993, a science teacher was prosecuted for failing to adopt reasonable safety precautions or failing to take reasonable care for the health and safety of others in practical work known to be hazardous. It should be noted, however, that the failures resulted in major accidents and were, in both cases, a blatant disregard of safety precautions or safe working and not a minor misjudgment or ignorance of safety requirements.

> In order to facilitate communication, an employer may appoint safety officers in schools; head teachers, their deputies or other senior staff, often have safety as one of their responsibilities. Safety officers, appointed by the employer, must not be confused with statutory trade union health and safety representatives. In an institution, where safety representatives from two unions make a request, an employer is obliged to set up a safety committee which has considerable powers of investigation although no legal liability.

Teachers are also subject to civil law which imposes a duty of care; they could, for example, be sued by a parent for negligence.

2.2   Health and Safety Regulations

Handbook
Ch.2.1.2

A number of Regulations have been enacted under the *HSW Act*. These impose duties on employers to set in place safe systems of working. Three important sets of Regulations are discussed below. (Other Regulations are discussed elsewhere in specific contexts. For summaries of relevant Regulations, see the references quoted here.)

DfEE Safety
Ch.3

The Control of Substances Hazardous to Health (COSHH) Regulations

Handbook
Ch.2.2.2

The hazardous substances covered by these Regulations include those that are toxic, harmful, corrosive or irritant, harmful microorganisms and substantial quantities of any dust. The major requirement of these Regulations is that an assessment of the risks involved in using or producing hazardous substances must be carried out before work commences [see Ch. 3].

Hazcards
Micro
Topics
Haz Man

Most educational employers, at the suggestion of the Health and Safety Commission, have adopted the principle of requiring that model or general risk assessments are consulted by teachers and technicians to obtain details of restrictions and precautions that must be observed in activities involving hazardous substances in laboratories, preparation rooms and elsewhere. Such general risk assessments include materials published by the Association for Science Education, the CLEAPSS School Science Service, the Scottish Schools Equipment Research Centre and the

Department for Education and Employment (formerly Department of Education and Science/Department for Education) [see 1.2].

A further requirement of the Regulations is that fume cupboards must be tested for an adequate level of performance at least every 14 months.

The Management of Health and Safety at Work Regulations

DfEE Safety
Ch.3 & 4

SSERC 181

Handbook
Ch. 2.2.3,
2.2.7, 4.2.3,
5.2.1, 7.7

These Regulations extend the principle of risk assessment embodied in the *COSHH Regulations* to **all** hazards in the work place. They also require school and college employers to make arrangements for the **planning, organisation, control, monitoring and review** of safety management in science departments [see Ch. 3]. Further, the Regulations require the establishment of appropriate **training** for dealing effectively with emergency procedures, such as fighting a small laboratory fire and washing out eyes and also in using hazardous equipment safely. In most instances, employers will delegate the function for organising such training to heads of departments, but may well not have done so explicitly.

The Provision and Use of Work Equipment Regulations

Handbook
Ch. 2.2.5

SSERC 182

DfEE Safety
Ch.8

These Regulations govern new and existing equipment (though, for the latter, some parts do not come into effect until 1997). Their purpose is to ensure that equipment is safe in its construction and use, and is satisfactorily maintained. In future, new equipment will increasingly be found to carry a *CE* mark, indicating that it has been manufactured to meet a European standard. The use of *CE* marks on equipment is designed to permit free trade throughout the EU. European safety standards may be less stringent than existing British standards. It is not therefore essential that equipment with a *CE* mark is purchased or used but all such equipment should be at least as safe as items carrying the *CE* mark.

Equipment must be suitable for its intended use; thus, for example, items manufactured for the domestic, DIY market may **not** be safe for use in schools. Science teachers should ensure that equipment used in their departments will not present hazards to adults or pupils. Items purchased from reputable educational suppliers should not normally pose any problems.

For existing equipment it may **not** be necessary, even by 1997, to replace items by new models. If old equipment can be used safely, then it need not be taken out of service. For example, some existing models of centrifuge, which do not possess a mechanism to lock the lid until the rotor has stopped spinning, **can** still be used, though some modifications may be required. Advice on the suitability of older equipment can be obtained from CLEAPSS and SSERC.

2.3   Codes of Practice

Although the *HSW Act* and its various Regulations govern the health and safety measures required, it should be appreciated that health and safety legislation is very **general** and the law must therefore be **interpreted** in order to produce codes of practice for safe working in specific situations. There is much guidance available including materials from the Health and Safety Executive (HSE), ASE, CLEAPSS School Science Service and SSERC. In addition, many recommendations for action on aspects of health and safety have been made by the government, ie, DfEE (formerly DES or DfE) in England, SOED in Scotland, WO in Wales and DENI in Northern Ireland.

It should be noted, however, that there may sometimes be a mismatch between such guidance and instructions that are issued by employers. Teachers and technicians must always follow their **employers'** rules and must seek to achieve their educational objectives by means which do not lead to risks to the health and safety of themselves, colleagues or pupils. This may occasionally require that some educational objectives are temporarily abandoned until matters can be resolved to ensure compliance, eg, an activity is not carried out until a fume cupboard is repaired.

> If teachers consider that unduly severe restrictions have been placed upon them by their employers, or that arrangements made by employers fall short of what is needed, there is no reason why they should not seek to have these arrangements altered. The ASE would be happy to advise and to give support in suitable cases.
>
> There is a general duty placed on teachers, technicians or other employees to draw attention to situations which give them concern for safety. There will be occasions when this should be done in writing and a record kept of all such communications.

2.4 Checking Compliance with Employers' Rules and Safety Legislation

A number of people may be involved in checking whether health and safety requirements are being observed. Perhaps the most important 'visitors' are Inspectors of the Health and Safety Executive, ie, Factory Inspectors. They have the power, and the duty, to enter schools for inspections which may be routine, after an incident, or on request, possibly made anonymously. HSE inspectors are most likely to suggest improvements to arrangements. They may, however, issue an Improvement Notice (requiring matters to be remedied within a specified period) or, rarely, a Prohibition Notice (effectively banning activities from that instant until the unsatisfactory situation is rectified or there is a successful appeal against the Notice).

DfEE Safety Ch. 2

Handbook Ch. 2.1.3

> Improvement or Prohibition Notices might be issued, for example, where there is a risk of staff or pupils coming into contact with mains voltage, inadequate maintenance of fume cupboards or failure to provide or wear eye protection.

Questions about health and safety provision may also be raised during the course of educational inspections or during a visit from an employer's representatives, including science advisers, safety officers and governors (often together with trade union safety representatives).

In the very unlikely event that an HSE inspector were to consider prosecution, s/he would caution the alleged offender (as the police do) and then take a formal statement. In the event of an accident, teachers and/or technicians should **not** admit liability nor make a statement without first taking advice from their professional associations and/or employers.

Teachers and technicians should not feel inhibited about challenging the recommendations of school (eg Ofsted) or HSE inspectors. In some cases, the comments made or advice given may not always be appropriate. It is always worth checking with independent bodies with expertise on health and safety matters, such as the ASE, the CLEAPSS School Science Service or SSERC.

The vast majority of problems concerning health and safety which arise in schools can be resolved by discussion among the staff involved, referring to the many sources of information available. One of the main aims of health and safety legislation – and indeed of this book – is to alert teachers and technicians to hazards in the work about to be started. Most of the time, it will not be necessary to remove the hazard completely (ie, abandon the activity) but instead to take various precautions or adopt alternative strategies. In this way, hazards **are** encountered, but in a safe way, risks are reduced to minimal levels and accidents prevented. [See also 3.10, for reference to the need to educate pupils and students on health and safety matters.]

3 Managing Safety

3.1 The Head of Department as Manager

There are two aspects to managing safety — managing the staff, procedures and systems of work within a department, and managing the pupils within the laboratory. Both are considered in this section.

> The term "head of department" is intended to be generic, indicating those who have some organisational or line management responsibility for science in a school or college. It is not intended to imply any particular type of organisation and includes heads of science departments or faculties, heads of biology, chemistry or physics departments, the principal teacher for biology, chemistry, physics or science, the director of science studies or the subject co-ordinator for science. Similarly, the term "staff" means just that: teachers and technicians (including full-time and part-time, permanent and temporary). If parents or other adults sometimes assist in laboratories, then they too should be considered in this category, as should those working to support bilingual pupils or those with special needs.

In the past, heads of department have tended not to think of themselves as managers. Teachers have often been allowed to function autonomously within their classrooms and laboratories and there may be resentment and resistance at any attempt to direct or interfere. Heads of department have sometimes assumed, without firm evidence, that there is common practice in the way in which colleagues interpret documents and implement policies and that colleagues have appropriate levels of subject expertise. However reluctantly, heads of department are now firmly identified as part of the "middle management" of schools, with the role of supervising and monitoring their colleagues and ensuring they receive adequate training. Equally, the headteacher, or some other member of the senior management team, should supervise the work of the head of department, and the governing body[1] and/or the education authority should supervise the work of the headteacher. If this seems alien to the way in which schools have operated in the past, it is central to the operation of the *HSW Act* and the Regulations made under it [see Ch. 2]. Health and safety

Reprints
Sec. B

---

[1] Health & Safety Commission *The Responsibilities of School Governors for Health and Safety*, 1992, ISBN 0 11 886337 1

legislation has been framed with all work sectors in mind. Clear line management structures are required and education establishments must conform.

Sometimes the problems of managing safety can seem overwhelming, but often it is only a matter of formalising procedures which already take place. For example, having safety as a standing item on the agendas of departmental meetings will serve as a reminder about the need for regular up-dating and possible training. It will also allow staff to talk informally about dangerous occurrences. Training, sometimes, may not need to be much more than a short item at a departmental meeting, the outcomes of which are minuted. Measures will need to be taken to cater for staff who are not present (eg, because they are part-timers, or work mainly in other departments): careful minutes circulated to all those teaching the subject would be a start. Copies of such minutes should also be passed to senior management, for their reference or action.

3.2 Safety Policies

Employers, such as education authorities, or the governors of grant-maintained or independent schools and incorporated colleges are required, by the *HSW Act*, to have health and safety policies and, by the *Management Regulations* [see Ch. 2] to have "health and safety arrangements". Such health and safety arrangements should be an integral part of the management policy.

Where an employer operates on a number of sites (eg, an education authority with many schools) then it would be normal to have a separate safety policy for each site. Within a school, there is no specific legal requirement to have a policy for each subject area, but some employers may require or strongly encourage it. Even where they do not, it is in the interests of the head of department as manager to produce a document which defines the organisation of safety, the procedures and routines to be followed, the duties of individuals, etc. Any such policy should be seen and approved by the governing body.

A science department safety policy might contain the following sections.

<table>
<tr><td>

Reprints
Sec. B

</td><td>

- A general statement about the *HSW Act*, the need to co-operate with the employer's health and safety requirements and how the policy relates to whole school policies
- A list of duties assigned to particular named members of the senior management and of the science staff (eg, safety in lower school science, safety in chemistry, the Radiation Protection Supervisor [see 12.8], induction of new technicians, etc).
- A statement about the approach to risk assessment.
- A statement about the induction procedures for new staff, and the on-going training requirements of all existing staff.
- A list of do's and don'ts for all staff, both teachers and technicians (ie, rules on such matters as locking laboratories, obtaining risk assessments for new procedures, etc).

</td></tr>
</table>

- A statement of procedures to be followed by non-science staff (including support staff) when registering classes or teaching in laboratories.
- A set of laboratory rules for pupils, perhaps supplemented by guidance on how and when they are to be taught, recalled and reinforced.
- A list of the regular checks required (eg fume cupboards, autoclaves, radium sources), their frequency, the procedures used, and who does them.
- A list of safety resources, including reference texts.
- Any specific safety requirements of the employer (eg, any local bans on particular procedures or chemicals).
- Emergency procedures, including immediate remedial measures which all staff are expected to take before first aid arrives.

A fuller discussion of the requirements of a safety policy will be found in *Safety Reprints*. It also features strongly in courses run by ASE INSET Services: *Management of Safety: A Course for Heads of Science* [see 1.5].

3.3 Training for Staff

Reprints
Sec. B

Under the *HSW Act*, and spelled out much more clearly in the *Management Regulations*, there are definite requirements to provide training for both teachers and technicians (or indeed other staff who might be affected, such as cleaners):

- when new staff are recruited (ie, induction),
- if their role changes (eg, a physicist starts teaching chemistry),
- in the use of particularly hazardous equipment (eg, the high-voltage transmission line demonstration),
- when new equipment or procedures are introduced,
- in emergency procedures.

Such training must be repeated periodically and must take place during working hours and take account of the needs of part-time staff.

Most, and quite possibly all, such training can be school-based. Induction of new but experienced staff may amount to not much more than issuing the departmental handbook or safety policy, together with comments such as "These are our arrangements for risk assessments ...", "The cut-offs for gas, water and electricity are located ...". The head of department must, however, check that those concerned fully understand what is expected of them. Newly-qualified teachers will need a more thorough induction, for example a regularly time-tabled meeting at which the following week's lessons can be discussed.

Some practical activities may require specific training (eg, microbiology or radioactivity). If these are highlighted in the scheme of work, then this may act as a trigger to ensure that the activity is not carried out by less-experienced or non-specialist staff without training and/or the consent of the head of department. The *Management Regulations* require regular training in emergency procedures, such as how to rinse out eyes following an accident [see 17.2].

Supply teachers and non-science staff covering science lessons also require training as do staff supporting bilingual pupils or those with special needs. This may amount to no more than a few brief comments at the start of the lesson, although a simple handout summarising laboratory do's and don'ts may be useful. More substantial training is likely to be required if a science supply teacher is to carry out practical work or if, exceptionally, a non-scientist is required to teach science regularly (eg, for timetable reasons). In Scotland, all teachers of science in secondary schools must be science graduates and, in addition, those teaching a specialist science subject need to have spent a minimum time at undergraduate level in that subject. There is no such requirement elsewhere in the UK. Exact training requirements will depend upon the individual's background, as well as the course(s) to be taught. In some cases, the head of department may feel the burden imposed by having to deliver such training is unreasonable: in such circumstances, as training is ultimately the employer's responsibility, the head of department should put her/his concerns in writing to the employer.

Students on initial teacher training are in a somewhat different position. A safety training programme needs to be set up. Safety should feature prominently in lesson planning and lessons need to be planned and talked through well in advance. The regular class teacher should be present in the laboratory for the first few lessons, until s/he is satisfied that the student can be left alone with the class. Even then, an experienced teacher should remain within earshot and should check from time to time that all is well. On any occasion on which the teacher or mentor decides that the risk warrants it, they should be prepared to stay with the class. It should be clear to the student when this is the case, since safety must be of prime importance.

Training is also needed for technicians. As with teachers the amount and type of training will depend upon the qualifications and experience of the individual and the nature of the work they are being asked to do. Much of it may well be school-based, eg with an experienced teacher or technician supervising the work of a new-comer.

3.4   Risk Assessments

A risk assessment is required whenever harmful microorganisms are used, hazardous chemicals are used or made (the *COSHH Regulations*), or before any hazardous activity is undertaken (mainly under the *Management Regulations*). The provision of a risk assessment is an employer's responsibility, although the **task** of assessing the risks will normally be delegated to employees. It is for employers to lay down what is required and the duty of the teacher or technician is to comply with such requirements, although sometimes employers seem unaware of their responsibilities and, in effect, try to "pass the buck" to the science department. While an employer can certainly ask for advice from employees and can delegate to them the task of assessment of risk, the legal responsibility still remains with the employer. Where an employer has failed to give clear guidance or failed to delegate particular tasks clearly and explicitly, it would be prudent for a science teacher to adopt practices common elsewhere in the educational system and to inform the employer in writing of the action taken, being sure to retain a copy.

Hazcards
Haz Man
Handbook
Topics
Micro

Most education employers, following guidance from the HSE[2], have adopted various national publications [see margin] as the basis for general risk assessments [see 2.2]. Before carrying out an activity, teachers should assess the risks, usually by consulting the employer's general risk assessments. Risk assessment, when planning a lesson, therefore is a thinking process, involving a comparison between a general risk assessment provided by the employer and the particular circumstances of the class to be taught and the room to be used. A few employers require schools to write down every hazardous chemical used in science and every use made of them. While this approach is common in industry, it is **not** expected by the HSE in schools, although teachers, as all employees, must co-operate with their employers on all matters of safety. General risk assessments, by their very nature, have already been written down: there is little point in doing so again. What schools **must** do, however, is to be able to produce evidence for HSE Inspectors or others that the department has actually consulted the general risk assessments and considered how they should be implemented in the range of courses taught. Sometimes, for example, local conditions may require a **greater** level of restriction ("I wouldn't do that with 11D!"), but schools cannot adopt a **less** restrictive approach than that required by the general risk assessment. Where schools find that a proposed activity is not covered by a general risk assessment, or where the requirements cannot be implemented (for example, because there is no working fume cupboard), then a special (or novel) risk assessment is required, and employers should have defined how this is to be obtained. [See also 3.11 for problems related to risk assessment for open-ended and investigative work].

> Often, if the employer is a member, special risk assessments will involve contacting CLEAPSS, or in Scotland, SSERC. *Preparing COSHH Risk Assessments for Project Work in Schools*, published by SSERC, gives excellent guidance and includes worked examples, together with Appendices giving information on carcinogens, sensitisers, materials for protective gloves, etc.

Reprints
Sec. B

One particularly useful procedure for showing that general risk assessments have been consulted is for schools to annotate "point-of-use" texts, ie schemes of work, syllabuses, teachers' and technicians' guides, etc. Annotation might involve high-lighting hazard warnings and precautions, the substitution of safer alternatives, noting down particular problems ("Remember to swop rooms for access to a fume cupboard"), drawing attention to the need for inexperienced staff to have hands-on

---

[2] Health and Safety Commission, *COSHH: Guidance for Schools*, 1989, HMSO, ISBN 0 11 885511 5

training, etc. Most responsible publishers these days have their texts checked for safety, but hazard warnings in published texts should be taken only as a flag, drawing attention to the need for the school to carry out an assessment of risks. A head of department or delegated representative needs to check through such texts to ensure that what is suggested does indeed coincide with what the employer permits and preferably to highlight particular hazards as indicated above.

3.5   Regular Checks

Employers have a duty to make arrangements to check the condition of various items from time to time: Table 3.1 summarises the position. In some cases, specific regulations require checking to take place, in other cases there is a more general requirement under the *HSW Act*, or at least a strong suggestion in official (governmental) guidance. In other cases it would simply be considered good practice, a part of the management function. In some schools, carrying out certain checks (eg on the air-flow

Table 3.1

Che'ck	Frequency	Legal status
Fume cupboards	At least every 14 months (effectively annually)	Specific requirement under *COSHH Regulations*
Contamination of radium sources Damage to any sealed radioactive source [In Scotland, leakage of all sealed sources]	Every few years (but annual may be more practicable) Visual check every time used [Every two years (but annual may be more practicable)]	Specific requirement under *Ionising Radiation Regulations*, interpreted in DESAM 1/92. [Interpreted in SOED *Circular 1166 (1987)*]
Portable mains-operated electrical equipment	Dependent on use	Specific requirement under *Electricity at Work Regulations*
Autoclaves, model steam engines & pressure cookers	As specified in the written Scheme of Examination drawn up by a competent person	Specific requirement under *Pressure Vessel Regulations*
Chemicals with a short safe shelf-life	Annual	General duties under *HSW Act*
General laboratory fixtures & fittings, equipment, etc.	A checklist should be drawn up of items to be checked daily, weekly, termly or annually	General duties under *HSW Act*

rates in fume cupboards) may not be the responsibility of the science department but any departmental policy should state where the responsibility lies. For those which **are** a departmental responsibility, the policy should state the frequency of checks, name staff responsible, and indicate the procedure to be adopted. There should also be a log book, or some other record-keeping system. Often, education employers will not have made a specific delegation of the duty to check, but it would be prudent for a head of department to assume it anyway and inform the employer in writing of the action taken.

> Under various regulations, specific duties are placed on "competent persons". School teachers and technicians sometimes wonder whether they are competent to carry out these duties, including some of the checks in Table 3.1, and whether they might be held responsible in the event of a subsequent accident involving a piece of equipment they had checked. In fact, HSE has made it clear that it is the employer who has ultimate responsibility. A technician who completes a test record sheet is simply indicating that a test has been carried out according to a set procedure, and that to the best of her/his knowledge and belief, the condition was as recorded on the sheet. Unless technicians are deliberately negligent they would have nothing to fear from signing the form.

3.6 Monitoring Safety

Having set up appropriate procedures and policies, the head of department needs to monitor their implementation. This needs to be done as sensitively and informally as possible. Log books will show whether safety checks are being carried out in accordance with policy. Occasional monitoring of technicians' requisition sheets may indicate whether risk assessment procedures are being followed, as will discussions at departmental meetings. Visits to lessons, both informal when delivering a message, or in more formal lesson observation, eg, as a part of appraisal, will be necessary. Discussion with colleagues to whom tasks have been delegated will show what progress has been made. A clear expectation for teachers to follow the departmental scheme of work, and the risk assessments built in to it, should in the long run mean that compliance becomes almost automatic and any non-compliance very obvious.

> The head of department needs to be aware that old habits die hard. Gaining the co-operation of reluctant colleagues needs to be handled sensitively but firmly. If informal discussions do not bear fruit, then more formal warnings (involving senior management) may have to be considered, ultimately leading to disciplinary action. There is a legal obligation on employees to co-operate with their employers on safety matters but a confrontational approach is rarely successful among fellow professionals.
>
> Particular care needs to be taken to monitor the work of new members of staff, and students in training, to ensure that they fully understand what is expected of them. In the case of newly- qualified teachers, as a part of the induction of new staff, time should be set aside on a regular basis for

meetings with one or more experienced members of the department in which the teaching programme can be discussed in advance, to ensure that hazards are fully appreciated. Similar steps will be necessary with students on initial teacher training, licensed or authorised teachers and newly-appointed technicians.

3.7   Access to Laboratories and Supervision of Pupils

School science laboratories, preparation and storage rooms, should be considered as "danger areas" under the *Management Regulations*. This means access should be restricted by locking doors. This may not always be practicable when equipment is being moved around and increased vigilance will be needed at such times. Sometimes there can be a conflict between security requirements and fire escape routes. A school might be legally liable if, through lax security, a pupil was able to steal chemicals and then injured her- or himself as a result. Any compromise is likely to depend on the detailed geography of a particular department, and should be recorded in the safety policy.

Pupils should normally be allowed to work in laboratories only under the supervision of qualified science teachers, ie, those with a teaching certificate or degree in which a science subject formed a substantial part of the course, usually the main subject. Where laboratories have to be used as form rooms, arrangements need to be negotiated with the headteacher. It is essential that the form in question should be one which could reasonably be expected to behave appropriately. In addition, it is highly desirable that the form tutor should be a scientist. If this cannot be arranged, then the head of department, or a delegated representative, needs to give some training to the teacher concerned, for example, about security and laboratory rules. It might be sensible to have a simple one-page handout. Similar steps will be necessary if, exceptionally, a non-science subject has to be taught in a laboratory, or if a non-scientist is covering a lesson in a laboratory. Some employers have a rule that whenever there is a non-scientist in a laboratory, a qualified science teacher must be within earshot and aware of what is going on.

Pupils, however senior, should not be allowed to work unsupervised in laboratories, although in the case of students on advanced level GCE or GNVQ courses (or, in Scotland, Certificate of Sixth Year Studies), or pupils using photographic darkrooms etc, it may be sufficient to have a science teacher or, if appropriate, technician within earshot, ie, in an adjoining room. Before allowing this to happen, however, a risk assessment should be carried out. The teacher needs to be satisfied that s/he knows what the students are doing, that the risks have been identified and adequately controlled, that the students fully understand what they are expected to do, are competent to do it, and are sufficiently reliable and mature to be permitted this limited degree of autonomy. Even so, the teacher should be present during any particularly hazardous stages. The headteacher should be aware of these arrangements, and have given general approval to them, for example as a part of the departmental safety policy.

3.8 Technicians and Other Non-teaching Staff

There are many highly competent technicians in schools. However, there are also many with few formal qualifications, and little experience. Too many of the accidents reported in school science involve technicians in some way. New teachers, particularly, tend to be unaware that some technicians have only limited understanding of science. In addition, technicians may often be working alone, for example, during holiday periods, and risk assessments should take this into account. All employees have a responsibility for each others" safety. This means that teachers need to be careful to anticipate the hazards to which technicians might be exposed (eg, when diluting concentrated acids), warn them, especially if they are inexperienced, and, where necessary, instruct them in the appropriate safe technique. It also means that technicians have a duty to point out to teachers any hazards they may notice in particular practical work, or in a piece of apparatus. Where this is difficult, the head of department should be informed. This is not "interfering" – it is what the law requires. However, the head of department should try to ensure that it is done sensitively, to avoid intra-departmental conflict. In this context, it is helpful if technicians attend departmental meetings, especially when safety is on the agenda.

Both teachers and technicians have a duty towards other employees, and, indeed, any visitor, who may enter the laboratories. This includes taking account of the activities of cleaners and caretakers, external contractors and visitors on open days (where occasionally there can be a rather hair-raising disregard for safety). Equipment and chemicals should be left in as safe a condition as reasonably practicable at the end of a day's work. This does not mean that everything must be removed from the laboratory, but care should be taken in the disposal of chemicals, and clearing up spills, broken glass, etc. Broken glass should be wrapped, and there should be dedicated, clearly labelled receptacles for it. There should be warnings on any hazard where it is not immediately obvious. Equipment left running overnight (other than that designed to run continuously, eg aquaria) should carry an appropriate label.

Topics
Ch. 5b

3.9 Class Size

Except in Scotland, where class sizes for all practical subjects (including science) must not exceed 20, there is no statutory limitation on class size in any subject. However, custom and practice over many years have tended to result in smaller classes for technology subjects than for science. Sometimes, there are local agreements between the employer and teachers' organisations. The optimum number in a science class will depend upon the age, ability, and degree of responsibility of the pupils, the type of work being attempted, the nature of the laboratory and the experience of the teacher. Thus for some classes, three might be too many, while a lecture can be delivered as safely to 50 as to 15 pupils. A survey in

England and Wales, published in 1994[3] suggested average class sizes were 25.2 at Key Stage 3, and 20.8 at Key Stage 4. ASE policy[4] is that group size should be limited to a maximum of 20 at Key Stages 3 and 4, and 14 for post-16 work.

There is no direct evidence that more accidents occur in larger classes, possibly because teachers are more inclined to limit practical work in such situations, with the result that pupils' education suffers. There are particular difficulties in adequately supervising open-ended projects and investigative work [see 3.11].

DfEE Safety Ch. 11.2

Laboratory size is also an important factor. Cost limitations mean that most new laboratories are likely to have an area of about 80–85 m^2. A useful rule of thumb suggests there should be 2 m^2 of "free floor area" for each 11-year old, rising to 3 m^2 for 16-year olds. In addition, each pupil needs a minimum of about 0.36 m^2 of work surface. Distances between work spaces are also important.

If, in a teacher's professional judgement, a class is too large, or a laboratory too cramped, to attempt a particular practical activity safely, then other strategies need to be considered. These might include abandoning the activity, having only part of the class doing practical work at any one time, adopting pupil-assisted teacher demonstrations, swopping rooms, etc. Some strategies may affect the teacher's ability to deliver the National Curriculum properly. If the problem persists, a class teacher should consult the head of department; it may be necessary to inform the headteacher in writing, and to involve a teachers' trade union or equivalent.

3.10 Discipline in the Laboratory

The foundations of laboratory safety are clean and tidy habits, adoption of good laboratory practice, good discipline, the strict prohibition of unauthorized practical work, the teacher's knowledge and understanding of the hazards involved and, above all, the example set by the teacher. Pupils need to be trained in good laboratory practice [see 4.3]. Lessons that are well planned, well organised and in which all pupils are kept actively engaged throughout, are much more likely to be safe.

As part of its safety policy, the department should have an agreed set of laboratory rules, although these could vary according to the age, ability and degree of responsibility of the pupils. They should be clear and concise [see 4.3]. The rules should be issued to pupils and/or posted on laboratory walls. They also need to be **taught**. The reasons behind them should be explained when they are issued and there need to be frequent

---

[3] Borrows, P., "Science Departments in Secondary Schools: a Survey", *Educ. Sci.*, 1994, (157), 24–25.

[4] *ASE Policy: Present and Future: Class Size*, 1991, ASE

reminders. Hazards specific to a particular activity should be explained as a matter of course. Any worksheets used should draw attention to hazards, and give details of appropriate safety measures. Pupils are more likely to follow safety requirements if they understand why they are necessary, and particularly if they have been involved in developing them. Safety should be a normal part of pupils' reports on any practical activity.

It is essential that the science department has a clear discipline structure, which is understood by all concerned. In some schools there are, regrettably, pupils whose lack of motivation and self-control makes them a danger to themselves and to others, particularly when practical work is in progress under the direction of a less-experienced or less-skilful teacher. Science departments need a clear policy on how to cope with such pupils and asking for help should in no way be seen as a failure on the part of an individual teacher. It may be necessary to remove disruptive pupils temporarily, for example by placing them in the classes of more-experienced teachers. In extreme cases, the National Curriculum may have to be disapplied, or the pupil may be unable to complete assessed coursework. Whatever strategy is adopted, it must conform with the procedures generally agreed within the school.

3.11 Open-ended Projects and Investigative Work

Increasingly, open-ended projects and investigations are finding a place in school science, for example in the National Curriculum in England and Wales, in GNVQ courses and in the Scottish Certificate of Sixth Year Studies. Supervision of project work can present problems [see 3.7], and it can be difficult to assess the risks. Pupils should be encouraged to act *as if* they were the employer by identifying the hazards and analysing the risks: a pro forma sheet may be useful in giving them a structure to work to. Even so, particular care is needed to ensure that they have had their plans approved by the teacher before practical activity starts, to be certain that the risk assessment meets the employer's requirements and the control measures are adequate. As plans often change during an investigation, it is wise to restrict the contexts for investigative work to those in which only relatively low-hazard chemicals, equipment and procedures are used, although to some extent this will depend on the age, experience and capability of the pupils and the level of the course.

> At the time of writing, the ASE is hoping to embark on a project intended to develop teaching materials to promote a greater awareness of safety both within and outside the laboratory, and to help pupils understand the process of risk assessment.

4 Safe Laboratory Practice

4.1 School Accident Statistics

School science laboratories, often considered by the general public including many non-science teachers as dangerous places, are relatively safe. The majority of injuries occur in or on school playgrounds, sports fields or gymnasia. Recent HSE statistics (Table 4.1) show that of the serious injuries to pupils in schools, less than 1% occur in science laboratories. This emphasises the attention given to safety by most science teachers most of the time. However, many of this small number of accidents could have been prevented, as could the larger number of less serious incidents which occur.

Table 4.1 *Major accidents to pupils in schools (%)* [1]

Sports Activities	38.5
Gymnasium	27.0
Playground	12.1
Corridors, stairs and cloakrooms	7.3
Classrooms	7.1
Extramural activities	1.5
Toilets etc	1.3
Science laboratories	0.9
Handicraft rooms and workshops	0.6
Domestic science	0.1
Other	3.7

4.2 Science Accident Statistics

Table 4.2 gives the most recent national statistics on accidents in science laboratories. Recent communications to both the ASE and CLEAPSS indicate a decrease in animal bites and instances of chemicals in the mouth, and a considerable increase in the frequency of injuries caused by inhalation of gases. Despite the improved use of eye protection, the number of reported eye injuries remains disturbingly high, often resulting

---

[1] From HSE statistics for 1991/2

from accidents when heating but also from teacher demonstrations and pupil indiscipline.

Eye injuries also commonly occur to pupils who have completed their practical work and removed their own eye protection while washing up or before others around them have finished. It is important, therefore, that all pupils normally continue to wear eye protection until all practical work is completed [see Ch. 7].

SSERC 164

Table 4.2 *Most common school laboratory accidents (%)*[2]

Chemicals in the eye	23
Chemicals on the skin	21
Cuts	20
Burns and scalds	15
Dropping, falling, slipping, lifting, knocking	7
Chemicals in mouth	4
Inhalation	4
Animal bites	3
Explosions	2
Fainting	2
Electric shock	1

4.3 Safe Laboratory Practice

The careful and consistent implementation of safe laboratory practice requires the following.

- **Good class control**
  Poor behaviour or inattentiveness leads to accidents and occasionally to deliberate malpractice. If class control is in doubt, seek advice from experienced colleagues before undertaking practical work.

- **Effective teacher understanding of the risk assessment**
  An assessment of risk is required for any activity which involves a hazard. Relevant general risk assessments must be consulted, understood and acted upon. Employers have a duty to ensure that teachers' and technicians' knowledge and understanding of safety is maintained, by attending appropriate in-service courses and keeping up to date with publications such as this one. When staff are working outside their original specialisms, general risk assessments should be consulted and advice sought from colleagues before undertaking unfamiliar work. The *Management Regulations* require training, which can be departmentally-based INSET, to be

DfEE Safety
Ch. 4, 8.3

Reprints
Sec. B

[2] Tawney, D., "Accidents in School Laboratories: a Report of an Investigation", *Educ. Sci.*, 1981, (95), 32–33.

given when employees take on new activities. Safety should be a standing item on the agenda of departmental meetings [see also Ch.3].

- **Well-understood rules and practices of safe working**

SSERC
164 & 168

  Pupils will need frequent reminders of rules and of even familiar techniques and practices, such as heating substances carefully or wearing eye protection. A quick teacher demonstration of a technique is a useful reminder. When the work demands eye protection, teachers should also wear it and insist on it being worn until all practical work is completed [see Table 4.3].

  Every department should have and display a set of laboratory rules for pupils. Table 4.3 is an illustrative list, which may be freely copied by purchasing institutions. However, it may need modification to make it appropriate for the pupils, circumstances and curricula of different departments. It will, of course, be necessary to spend some time explaining the rules and the reasons for them to every class [see 3.10].

- **Basic hygiene**

  This includes no eating or drinking in the laboratory except for tasting investigations where the precautions taken and instructions given should clearly indicate the special nature of the activity. Where possible, an alternative room, more suitable for the activity should be sought. Basic hygiene also includes careful attention to hand washing after handling chemicals, soil and plant, animal or microbial material. Laboratories should be equipped with supplies of soap, warm water if at all possible and paper, or other, towels so that hands can be dried hygienically. All spills should be cleared up promptly and benches and tables carefully wiped down at the end of lessons involving chemicals and microbes. Disposable paper towels should be provided for this purpose or if cloths are used they should be changed or washed frequently.

- **Laboratory tidiness**

  Laboratories should be kept free from clutter at all times. This particularly includes the following.
  - Coats and bags should be kept well out of the way, ideally in a designated area of the laboratory. DO NOT allow bags to clutter the floor. Pupils will need frequent reminders about this.
  - Equipment left over from previous practical activities should be cleared away as soon as possible or stored compactly and tidily.

Topics
Ch. 5b

  - Longer-term investigations left on side benches should be positioned out of the way if possible, with any hazards clearly labelled.
  - Piles of pupils' exercise books for marking or text books should not be allowed to accumulate on work surfaces, including the teacher's bench.

Table 4.3

LABORATORY RULES

The biggest danger in the lab. is **YOU!** You are a danger whenever you are either ***ignorant*** or ***careless*** or both. Remember this because the person most likely to suffer from your mistakes is **YOU!** Report any accident or breakage to your teacher.

1. Only enter a lab. when told to do so by a teacher. Never rush about or throw things in the lab. Keep your bench and nearby floor clear, with bags and coats well out of the way.

2. Follow instructions precisely; check bottle labels carefully and keep tops on bottles except when pouring liquids from them; only touch or use equipment and materials when told to do so by a teacher; never remove anything from the lab. without permission.

3. Wear eye protection when told to do so and keep it on until all practical work is finished and cleared away.

4. When using a Bunsen burner, make sure that ties, hair etc are tied back or tucked away.

5. When working with dangerous liquids or heating things, always stand so you can quickly move out of the way if you need to.

6. Never taste anything or put anything in your mouth in the laboratory. If you get something in your mouth spit it out at once and wash your mouth out with lots of water.

7. Always wash your hands carefully after handling chemicals or animal and plant material.

8. If you get burnt or a splash of a chemical on your skin, wash the affected part at once with lots of water.

9. Never put waste solids in the sink. Put them in the bin unless your teacher instructs you otherwise.

10. Wipe up all small spills and report bigger ones to your teacher.

- Animal cages, aquaria and potted plants should be arranged neatly and as far as possible away from areas used for pupil practical work.

- **Long hair**
  Long hair should be tied back and pupils with open styles warned that these can make hair more flammable.

Reprints
Sec. B

SSERC
169 & 170

- **Loose clothing**
  Ties, scarves and cardigans should not be allowed to hang freely as they can be a fire hazard or could catch apparatus or in machinery. Some materials, eg some jumpers and shell suits, can be particularly flammable. So too can laboratory coats made solely of lightweight synthetic fibres which are thus unsuitable.

- **Containers should be clearly labelled**
  Use correct names for the substances contained and a hazard symbol if appropriate. Pupils should be taught to use and recognise these. Previously used labels, which are no longer relevant, should be removed from containers to avoid confusion and danger.

Handbook
Ch. 9.6.2

- **Bunsen burners**
  Pupils should be taught and reminded how to use Bunsen burners correctly; to adjust them to a luminous flame when not being used and reminded that in direct sunlight even luminous flames are not very visible; to adjust the gas and air supplies to obtain a non-luminous, non-roaring flame 4–5 cm high, which is the kind normally required; to keep them a safe distance from blinds, posters etc; and to position them so that no pupil has to lean across the flame. Pupils should not be allowed to meddle with gas taps [see 6.1].

- **Techniques of heating**
  Pupils should be taught to heat substances correctly [see Ch. 6].

- **Smelling gases**
  Pupils should be shown, and reminded frequently, how to smell gases safely.

  Breathe in to fill the lungs with air. Pointing the test tube of gas away from the face at a distance of 15 cm, use the hand to waft the fumes towards the nose. Sniff gently (more will not be possible if the lungs are full of air). If no smell can be detected, slowly move the test tube closer to the face. Warn pupils not to take deep breaths.

- **Electrical switches**
  These should not be operated by anyone with wet hands. Pupils should be taught to switch off sockets before plugging in or unplugging appliances and should be warned against meddling with switches. Electric cables should not be allowed to trail dangerously when equipment is being used, transported or stored.

4.4 Some High Risk Situations

The number of occasions on which pupils are badly injured in science lessons is minute. Most accidents lead to no injury or to a relatively minor one, from which a rapid and complete recovery is made. Teachers should be aware that some activities pose risks to health, in particular risks to children or staff who suffer from asthma. The incidence of asthma is now reported to be as high as 14%, ie about 4 children in a class of 30, and schools should have a policy and procedures to take account of the needs of asthmatics.

Reprints
Sec. E

Asthma causes discomfort, distress, an inability or unwillingness to take part in certain activities in school and, of course, time off. There is considerable concern nationally about the impact of asthma on childrens' development and learning. One consequence of this concern is a concerted campaign to raise the general level of whole school and individual teacher understanding, so that appropriate policies for action are devised and training implemented.[3]

The list of known asthma triggers is quite extensive but in school science concern focuses on possible effects of inhaling particularly gases but also smoke and dusts from chemicals in the laboratory. Isocyanates and fumes from solder flux are known to be potent sensitisers [see 15.2] and it is important to control exposure to these. Other known sensitisers include pollen and dust from furry or feathery animals. Clearly exposure to these should be limited for all known asthmatics. Other than the general description "fumes", no chemicals or materials routinely used in secondary science are currently recognised as significant sensitisers. Organisations for asthmatics recommend that known sufferers should follow, as far as possible, a normal curriculum – asthma is controllable and pupils who suffer from it will know how to control it. Pupils diagnosed as asthmatic should have quick and easy access to prescribed medication for use in the event of an attack in the laboratory. For those pupils undiagnosed it is considered that laboratory chemicals, other than the two potent sensitisers given above, are unlikely to precipitate a first attack. The chances of an asthmatic pupil moving to secondary school without her/his asthma having been diagnosed must be small, so the most appropriate course of action for science teachers is to know and follow the school policy; be aware of the asthmatics in any class and how they should access their medication, and control their exposure to any known sensitisers or triggers. Furthermore all teachers should be alert to the identification of new relevant sensitisers.

Teachers and technicians may be expected to have greater exposure to potential sensitisers, for example, solder flux fumes. Staff therefore need to limit their own exposure to known or suspected sensitisers and should be aware of colleagues who are asthmatic [see 17.2].

SSERC 186

There are a few activities which present higher risks and seem to attract rather a high proportion of injuries. By understanding and avoiding such risks, teachers can make a significant impact on science safety. Although time on initial teacher training courses is limited, teachers in training

---

[3]   Further advice is available from: The National Asthma Campaign, Providence House, Providence Place, London N1 0NT; The National Asthma Training Centre, Winton House, Church Street, Stratford-upon-Avon CV37 6HB.

should be given hands-on experience of such high risk activities. In addition, heads of science should set up and monitor procedures to ensure that only staff who are adequately trained carry them out.

Demonstrations by the teacher tend to involve more hazardous activities than pupils would be allowed to carry out. For whatever reason, pupils are more likely to be seriously injured as a result of a teacher demonstration than by their own practical work. During demonstrations, pupils should be seated at a safe distance of 2 or 3 metres; remember too that they cannot quickly get out of the way when seated close together. Pupils should wear eye protection when the risk assessment determines it necessary and in many cases safety screens for pupils and teachers may also be needed.

Ethanol (alcohol) fires

There has been a significant number of accidents in which pupils were badly burned in fires resulting from the use of ethanol (alcohol, methylated spirits) as a fuel for model steam engines; solid fuels should be used. Other major and well-documented accidents have occurred when decanting or using hot ethanol too close (< 1 metre) to a lighted Bunsen burner.

Reprints
Sec. C

Hydrogen explosions

A mixture of hydrogen and air is explosive over the range 4 to 75% hydrogen. It can be ignited not only by a naked flame, but also by catalysts such as transition metals or their oxides at temperatures of 500 °C (below red heat). Thus if hydrogen is being used to reduce copper oxide, heating must NOT start until all the air has been flushed out of the apparatus. When hydrogen is required, it is probably safer to use a cylinder of compressed gas than to generate it chemically, since the larger volume available will flush the air out more efficiently. The volume of air in the apparatus should be minimised by, for example, avoiding the use of larger capacity vessels for drying agents. There is a fail-safe way of testing if the air has been flushed out: collect the issuing gases in an inverted test tube, and, still inverted, ignite it at a Bunsen burner 1 metre or more away. If all the air has been safely removed, the pure hydrogen will not explode, but will continue to burn silently for long enough to use as a torch to ignite the hydrogen issuing from the apparatus.

Reprints
Sec. C

SSERC 146

Chlorine preparation and use

Commonly, chlorine has been made in schools by dripping concentrated hydrochloric acid onto potassium manganate(VII) (permanganate) crystals. There have been several reported cases of concentrated sulphuric acid being used inadvertently − but disastrously − in place of hydrochloric acid, often because the sulphuric acid was on the bench to use as a drying agent. Despite the much greater density of sulphuric acid, and the fact that it does not fume, even experienced chemistry teachers have made this mistake. At the very least, alternative drying agents (eg silica gel) should be used, and preferably the chlorine should be made by dripping 5M hydrochloric acid into sodium chlorate(I) solution (hypochlorite).

Chlorine should only be prepared in a fume cupboard. Even quite small amounts can cause lung damage; some people may be much more sensitive than others and the effects may not be apparent for several hours or more. The ASE, CLEAPSS and SSERC have recently had a number of reports of

Reprints
Sec. C

chlorine poisoning in pupils. Two possible causes have been postulated; pupils are not taught how to smell gases correctly and instead inhale a relatively large amount of the gas; the increased incidence of asthma may indicate an increased susceptibility to gases such as chlorine. It is not yet clear whether these are valid suggestions but teachers are strongly advised to follow carefully advice in this and other safety publications on the handling and use of chlorine [see 15.3, 15.5].

The alkali metals

Reprints
Sec. C

The vigour with which the alkali metals (lithium, sodium, potassium) react with water constantly surprises teachers. Only rice-grain sized pieces of alkali metals should be used. Check that water from the tap is indeed cold. Lithium may explode if heated on pieces of porcelain or pottery.

Phosphorus

The rapid reaction of white phosphorus with air can trap the unwary. White phosphorus is easily ignited by the friction-generated heat from a knife cutting it; cut it under water, in a strong container such as a mortar.

The thermite reaction

The reaction is very vigorous and can shower sparks over several metres. Safety screens must be used, and pupils must be 3 or 4 metres away. Accidents have occurred when the mixture has been set off prematurely. A dry mixture of 6 g iron(III) oxide and 2 g powdered aluminium is sufficient. It can be carried out in a fireclay crucible set in dry sand, or in a beaker filled with dry kaolin, an indentation to hold the mixture being made in the kaolin with the end of a boiling tube. To initiate the reaction, use a pencil to make a hole in the thermite mixture and pour in 1.7 g of barium peroxide gently mixed with 0.2 g powdered magnesium. Insert a piece of magnesium ribbon sufficiently long to ensure that it can be lit and the teacher can move away before the reaction starts.[4]

High-voltage transmission demonstration [see 11.3]

Reprints
Sec. D

Handbook Ch.
12.9

Topics Ch. 3

SSERC 158

There have been several reported instances of teachers receiving a severe electric shock as a result of touching wires at mains voltage. The HSE is very concerned about this demonstration and teachers are strongly recommended to follow published advice on conducting it safely. In principle this advice is to limit voltages to 50 volts ac or less or to construct the apparatus in such a way as to ensure all conductors operating above 50 volts ac are fully insulated and cannot be touched. Serious shocks sometimes occur with voltages as low as 25 V ac which should be the maximum voltage for a class version of this practical.

Anaerobic cultures of microbes

Topics
Ch. 5a

Micro

Whenever cultures are grown in conditions of limited air supply there is a risk of anaerobic growth eventually occurring. In school microbiology this is most likely to happen in Petri dish agar plates which have been completely sealed with tape and left for some time. To prevent this the lids of Petri dishes should be taped down to the bases with 2 or 4 pieces of tape rather than around the rim. This will leave sufficient space for gases from the air to diffuse in and out of the dish [see Ch. 13].

---

[4] For an alternative method see *Science Equipment Bulletin 92*; Spring 1995 (CLEAPSS)

5 Fire Precautions

5.1 Aims

The aims of fire protection are:

Reprints
Sec. C

- to minimise the risk of a fire starting
- to allow the occupants to evacuate the area rapidly in the event of fire
- to minimise the risk of injury to fire fighters
- to minimise the subsequent damage in the event of a fire.

It is the prerogative of the relevant fire authority to give advice on fire precautions (such as means of escape).

5.2 Laboratory Design

DfEE Safety
Ch. 11,
Topics
Ch. 10 & 11

A number of factors relating to fire precautions need to be borne in mind when planning a laboratory. These include such things as

SSERC
162 & 171

- the number and location of exits
- the location of mains switches/valves for electricity/gas/water supplies,
- the siting of fire-fighting equipment [see below]
- the provision of tamper-resistant fittings (eg anti-rotation devices for gas taps [see 5.3])
- avoiding the use of plastics that are flammable and/or liable to melt for construction, storage containers and fittings (eg sinks, lampshades, etc)
- the siting of the stores for flammable chemicals and combustible materials as well as the manner in which flammable liquids and other potential fire hazards (eg alkali metals and phosphorus) are stored [see Ch.16 and 11.4].

Additional relevant advice and background information for those involved in the design of new or "re-modelled" laboratories is available in publications from the ASE[1], CLEAPSS, SSERC and the Architects Department of the DfEE[2,3].

DfEE Safety
Ch. 11

When planning a new laboratory, it is essential to consult the local Fire Prevention Officer at all stages so as to avoid any costly last-minute changes.

Haz Man

Each laboratory and preparation room should normally be provided with a fire blanket and a suitable extinguisher [see 5.4].

Fire-fighting equipment must conform to local requirements and must be regularly inspected and maintained by a competent person.

5.3   Routine Precautionary Measures

DfEE Safety
Ch. 5,
Handbook
Ch. 4.2.3
& 4.3

Teachers and laboratory staff should know the positions of fire extinguishers, emergency cut-offs and fire exits. The *Management Regulations* [see 2.2] require that staff should be trained in emergency procedures, for example, the use and limitations of fire extinguishers, sand and fire blankets. The holding of short regular practice drills for extinguishing small bench fires and clothing on fire is recommended [see 5.4].

Both staff and pupils should be familiar with the drill for the orderly evacuation of the building in the event of an emergency.

Waste bins should be of metal and emptied daily. Particular care should be taken to ensure that waste materials contaminated with dangerous residues (eg filter paper on which alkali metals have been cut) are suitably treated prior to disposal. Phosphorus residues must never be placed in waste bins.

SSERC 122

Charcoal blocks must be cooled completely, eg by immersion in cold water for several hours or stored in a metal container with an air-tight lid.

Haz Man

Reprints
Sec. C

Methylated spirits (ethanol) is the cause of the majority of reported fires; partly, no doubt, because of its widespread use in school laboratories. The fire risks associated with this relatively familiar substance should not be underestimated and appropriate precautions should **always** be taken with this as with other flammable liquids [see 4.4, 6.2].

---

[1]   *Building for Science – A Laboratory Design Guide*, ASE, 1989, ISBN 0 86357 119 0
[2]   *Fire and the Design of Educational Buildings*, DES Building Bulletin 7, 6th Edition, HMSO, 1988, ISBN 0 11 270585 5
[3]   *Science Accommodation in Secondary Schools*, Department for Education, HMSO, 1995, ISBN 0 11 270873 0

Reprints
Sec. B

SSERC 171

Handbook
Ch. 4

DfEE Safety
Ch. 5,
Haz Man

Handbook
Ch. 4.1.4

Damage to gas supply lines, including bench gas taps, should result in immediate action. Particular vigilance is required where light-weight island service bollards, moveable tables with overhead services and bottled gas (lpg) supplies are used. Flexible connections (eg Bunsen tubing) should be regularly checked and replaced if there is evidence of damage or poor fit. Any smell of unburnt gas should be investigated immediately and dealt with before classes continue.

5.4   Dealing with Laboratory Fires

The safety of people should always be paramount. In the case of a major fire, an infrequent occurrence in schools while they are in session, priority must be given to the evacuation of pupils, staff and visitors. Apart from shutting off mains electricity switches and gas supplies (if this can be done quickly and safely), school staff should only attempt to tackle small fires that may easily be brought under control in a minute or so.

However, most fires arising from laboratory accidents are small and easy to control. The majority are generally best dealt with by smothering with a fire blanket or fire-proof mat (or merely allowing the fire to burn itself out). It is frequently preferable to avoid using a fire extinguisher. Staff should be aware of the force with which the gas may be expelled from carbon dioxide fire extinguishers and, if a fire extinguisher is used, take great care to avoid making matters worse by knocking over beakers etc.

Any extinguisher must be used with extreme care in the vicinity of animal enclosures, particularly those types which use a fire-suppressant gas (eg carbon dioxide) or vapour (eg dense organic vapour) to smother the fire.

Note that carbon dioxide extinguishers should not be used on burning metals. Metal fires should be smothered with a large excess of clean **dry** sand and a suitable supply should be kept available for this purpose; this need not necessarily be in a "fire bucket". When experiments involving flammable metals are to be undertaken, the pack of sand included in the chemical spills kit [see 7.7] could be used for dealing with small fires of this type.

Following a metal fire, the resultant mixture should be allowed to cool and then treated in order to render any metal residues harmless.

Phosphorus fires can be extinguished by covering with sand and then adding water.

All fire-fighting equipment must be serviced as soon as possible after use.

If a person's clothes catch fire, lie the victim down on the ground immediately, keeping the flames on top and away from the face. Spread a fire blanket, thick garment or cloth over the flames to extinguish them. Do not roll casualties over or allow them to roll over themselves [see 17.3].

6 Heating Things

6.1 Heat Sources

Handbook
Ch. 11.6

Most eye injuries have occurred when heating is in progress, so eye protection should be worn during any activity where the risk assessment requires it [see 7.1].

Pupils should be reminded of the need to check that materials and objects that have been heated, including tripods, gauzes, electric hot plates, immersion heaters, beakers, etc have cooled sufficiently before making any attempt to handle them. This is particularly important when clearing up in a hurry.

The Bunsen burner will probably always be the chief heat source in most school laboratories and pupils should be taught how to use it properly [see 4.3].

A roaring flame should only be used when really necessary and **never** to heat a liquid in a test tube [see also 6.2 below].

Handbook
Ch. 8.1.2,
9.6.4, &
9.6.5

Adequate maintenance of both burners and the gas supply is essential for the satisfactory and safe operation of Bunsen burners. Blockages in the supply, jet, mixing tube and flame-retention collar should be investigated and dealt with without delay and faulty burners withdrawn from service until the defects have been remedied.

SSERC 171

Contrary to some beliefs, ordinary rubber tubing is acceptable for use with Bunsen burners, although it may have a limited life.

SSERC 172

Bunsen burners are available that operate on liquefied petroleum gases (lpg, ie butane, propane, etc) but Fire Prevention Officers in some areas will not allow lpg in schools. This decision may be worth challenging if lpg is specifically required. Large cylinders require the display of warning signs [see 7.9].

SSERC 162

Gas taps are now available with pupil-resistant anti-rotation devices [see 5.3] and these are especially important when using lpg, since, in the case of a leak, the much denser gases tend to accumulate in traps and voids beneath suspended floors and to diffuse away much more slowly than natural gas. There is much to be said for using gas taps which lock in the off position and can readily be seen to be in that position.

Burners sold as camping stoves are unlikely to be appropriate for permanent use in laboratories, but may have a role in emergencies when a piped supply of gas is temporarily unavailable.

Spirit lamps should have a broad base to prevent overturning, and it is wise to stand them in a tray containing sand. Some types are safer than others[1].

Solid fuel burners may be used in place of spirit lamps and should be used with model steam engines. They avoid the dangers inherent in the use of liquid fuel and are available from camping shops. However both the two common solid fuels, hexamine and ethanol tetramer (metaldehyde), are toxic to some degree and should only be used in a well-ventilated space. Model steam engines designed to operate on lpg are also available.

SSERC 182

Electric hot plates with or without magnetic stirrers are excellent for heating liquids. Care, however, must be taken when heating flammable liquids with low auto-ignition temperatures [see 15.6].

Baths of hot water should be used for heating flammable liquids [see 6.2]. **Electric kettles** are convenient sources of hot water and their usefulness is often overlooked in the laboratory.

Electric heating mantles are ideal for refluxing and distilling flammable and other liquids. However, they are either fully "on" or fully "off" and this can lead to "bumping" even when anti-bumping granules are employed. This is a particular danger in the hydrolysis of esters using aqueous alkali, when vigorous continuous boiling, even using a Bunsen burner, is a safer technique.

SSERC 148

Electric lamps (infra-red lamps) can be used for evaporation and for heating small animal cages such as vivaria. They can ignite dried grass, paper and other combustible material and may explode if wetted. They should not, therefore, be left unattended when being used for drying or evaporation purposes.

Vivarium heaters, using infra-red radiation, provide a safe means of heating animal containers. They consist of strips or pads, which are applied to the base or rear panel of the container.

Horticultural heaters often used in propagators should be constructed to a very high safety standard. The simplest way of reducing electrical hazards is to fit their mains lead with a plug incorporating a residual-current device (RCD). However, these are limited in the protection they provide and should not be used to remedy inadequate designs.

Small, low-voltage immersion heaters have been known to explode as a result of the generation of steam inside them following a leak. This can be avoided by rejecting any heaters with damaged seals, which might allow water to enter. However, to avoid the problem of unnoticed defects, these heaters should not be allowed to cool with the seal under water.

Reprints
Sec. D

---

[1] "Heating for Junior and Middle School Science", *Educ. Sci.*, 1979, (85), 30.

SSERC
163, 169

Soldering irons of the low-voltage type are strongly recommended for pupil use. This avoids problems that occur if the insulation of the mains lead is melted by the hot bit and reduces the risk of insulation breakdown between the element and the circuit under construction.

6.2   Techniques of Heating

Pupils should become competent in the safe use and control of the prime source of heat used in their laboratories, usually a **Bunsen burner** [see 4.3]. Once taught, pupils will continue to need frequent reminders of appropriate techniques.

Heating activities should normally be conducted standing up so that the pupil or teacher can quickly take evasive or other action if necessary.

When heating solids in test-tubes, the tube should be held almost horizontally with the solid forming a shallow layer along the tube to prevent blockage (see *Fig. 6.1*).

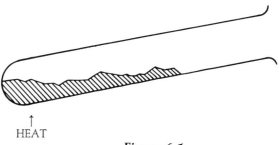

↑
HEAT

Figure 6.1

Pupils should be taught to point test tubes away from both their own faces and those of their neighbours. Teachers and pupils should be alert to the possibility of

(i)   particles of solid being forcibly ejected from within the heated material as a result of "decrepitation" and

(ii)   the production of steam and/or hazardous gases.

Small quantities of solids may also be heated in combustion spoons, ceramic paper, tin lids or beer-bottle tops ("crown corks" with the lining burnt out). Aluminium (eg milk-bottle tops) may melt or react with the substance being heated and should not be used. Asbestos paper is also unsuitable for use [see 15.4].

Reprints
Sec. C

When heating test tubes or flasks fitted with corks or bungs carrying delivery tubes, the apparatus should be checked continually to ensure that blockages are not being created by any solid matter within the apparatus, melting rubber, etc. Where the "open" end of a delivery tube is immersed in water or other liquid, steps to avoid "sucking back" must be taken *immediately* heating is stopped or just prior to doing so.

Reprints
Sec. C

Lithium should not be heated on ceramic paper, crucible lids or similar materials [see 4.4, 15.6].

When heating liquids, test tubes should never be more than a quarter full and it is preferable to use a wide tube (ie a boiling tube), which is held at an angle of about 45° or less to the horizontal. A small flame should be used and the tube continually shaken while being moved rapidly in and out of the flame.

The avoidance of "bumping" can be achieved by the addition of pieces of broken pot or special anti-bumping granules, which promote smooth boiling. Anti-bumping material should only be added to a cold liquid. If there is a need to add it to a liquid that has already been heated, the liquid should be removed from the heat and allowed to cool for several minutes, otherwise it may boil over.

When solutions are to be evaporated "to dryness", great care is needed to avoid the violent ejection of solid material ("spitting") at a point when most of the solvent has evaporated. This demands the gentlest of heating, such as can be provided by the use of a "water" or "steam bath" (see "Heating flammable liquids" below).

Heating flammable liquids [see 15.6] is the most common cause of fires in school laboratories. The liquids concerned are, most commonly, ethanol (alcohol or methylated spirit) [see 5.3], heptane, ethoxyethane (diethyl ether) or other ethers, methylbenzene (toluene), 1,2-dimethylbenzene (xylene) and propanone (acetone).

Many serious accidents have involved the use of ethanol as a fuel in burners for model steam engines. A solid fuel [see 6.1], in a specially designed burner, should therefore be used in place of ethanol for this purpose.

Flammable liquids should never be heated directly by a naked flame. The following technique is recommended when a hot flammable solvent is required, such as in the extraction of chlorophyll from plant material.

Reprints
Sec. C & F

Handbook
Ch. 7.4.3,
DfEE Safety
Ch. 14

- Use an electric kettle to provide water close to boiling point.
- Choose an evaporating basin to hold the solvent and a beaker with a diameter just smaller than that of the basin to act as a water bath. For very small quantities, a boiling tube may be used in place of the evaporating basin (see *Fig. 6.2*).
- If necessary, lag the beaker with a strip of carpet felt, expanded polystyrene wall insulation or other material and pour in sufficient water to make contact with most of the evaporating basin when it is resting on top of the beaker.
- If the extraction or dissolving is not complete when the water in the beaker has become too cool, replace it with more hot water.

Many solvents can be made to boil by this technique.

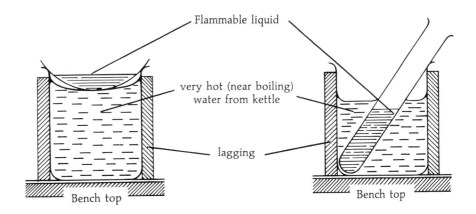

Figure 6.2

7 Safety Equipment and Other Safety Measures

DfEE Safety
Ch. 14

7.1 Eye and Face Protection

Topics
Ch. 2,
Reprints
Sec. B

Protective spectacles, goggles or face shields, to the relevant British Standard, must be worn in all circumstances whenever the risk assessment points to a risk of damage to the eyes or face; failure to do so could be regarded as negligence. It is essential that teachers, pupils, technicians and visitors to the laboratory (eg on 'Open Days') all comply with this basic requirement.

Eye protection must always be worn when heating chemicals, handling chemicals classed as hazardous (ie corrosive, toxic, irritant, harmful, etc), when carrying out potentially exothermic reactions or operations likely to give rise to flying fragments of material.

> Whenever eye protection is required, it should continue to be worn by all until **everyone** has finished the relevant activity. Pupils are still vulnerable to the results of unforeseen incidents occurring nearby where practical work is still in progress.

Teachers need to ensure that the eye protection provided is actually worn and **worn over the eyes**.

Although safety spectacles provide less protection than goggles, pupils are generally more willing to wear them. In many circumstances, therefore, they may be safer than goggles because of the better visibility they provide and the greater likelihood that they will be worn. However, for wearers of spectacles or when handling alkali solutions more concentrated than 0.5 M, concentrated acids, bromine and corrosive or toxic chemicals, goggles are recommended. Ordinary spectacles do not, in general, offer sufficient protection to be considered suitable on their own.

Handbook
Ch. 3.2

SSERC
164 & 168

Handbook
Ch. 3.2.4

> The exact policy on the provision of eye protection will vary from school to school. Most will provide class sets of safety spectacles for normal use but, in addition, enough goggles should be available to equip at least a full class. The system(s) for storing eye protection, especially safety spectacles, should ensure that the risk of scratching the lenses is minimised.

All eye protection should be cleaned regularly by washing at least termly with correctly diluted detergents or a surface-active ampholytic disinfectant. Eye protection should also be regularly checked for scratching and other damage and replaced as necessary. Post-16 students could be encouraged to purchase goggles for their exclusive use.

The hazard of alkalies to the eyes is greater than that of acids of comparable concentration [see 15.7]. Below the sixth form, for most purposes there is no need to use alkali more concentrated than 0.5 M, which is much less hazardous.

In addition, risks to the eyes can arise in unexpected circumstances such as the stretching of elastic materials (eg nylon thread) and during dissection, when detached pieces of bone or cartilage may be flicked towards the face. Special eye protection may be needed when exposure to short-wave ultraviolet radiation occurs. However, it is not necessary when using the lasers normally used in schools [see 12.4].

An accident has been reported in which a long length of elastic strap from a pair of goggles caught fire as a pupil leant over a Bunsen flame. Loose straps should therefore be securely tucked in (as with ties and other loose clothing [see 4.3]).

Handbook
Ch. 3.2.4

Pictures taken, eg for publicity purposes, should show full compliance with relevant safety precautions.

7.2   Protective Clothing

It is advisable to wear suitable protective clothing whenever practical work is being carried out and essential when using microorganisms at sixth-form level or open radioactive sources.

It is not common for schools to provide laboratory coats or aprons but pupils, particularly sixth-form students, should be encouraged to provide their own. Laboratory coats and aprons are especially desirable if there is a risk of splashing corrosive liquids (although coats tend to protect the clothes rather than the person).

Protective coats and aprons made solely from lightweight synthetic materials (nylon, polyester, terylene, etc) are not suitable for laboratory use owing to their inherent fire risk [see Ch. 5].

Suitable protective gloves may sometimes be needed by teachers and technicians, and especially when:

- washing apparatus contaminated with unknown or hazardous chemicals, or if there are concerns over skin conditions
- handling some chemicals when the risk assessment requires it, although care should be taken to ensure that glassware does not slip and cause an even greater hazard
- handling chemicals known to sensitise the skin and to cause allergic reactions
- handling hot apparatus where it cannot be allowed to cool
- handling untamed and wild mammals, birds or reptiles.
- handling contaminated animal litter (use disposable gloves)

In some situations it will be appropriate for pupils to wear protective gloves.

Care needs to be taken over the choice of gloves. Many types are penetrated by particular solvents in a few seconds and it is more dangerous to wear the wrong type of glove than no gloves.[1]

Handbook
Ch. 10.4

7.3 Safety Screens (Explosion Screens)

Haz Man

Securely fixed safety screens should be employed during any demonstration in which there is a known, or suspected, risk of explosion, or implosion.

It is unlikely that one screen will be sufficient to enclose apparatus to protect both teacher and pupil [see 15.7, 15.8].

A fume cupboard should not be used as an explosion screen.

7.4 Safe Use of Pipettes

All mouth pipetting should be avoided; some form of mechanical pipette filler should always be used.

Pupils should be taught to hold the pipette only a centimetre or so from the end when inserting it into the filler to avoid breaking the glass and not to push too hard or too far [see 8.1].

7.5 Safety in Transport

Large bottles containing dangerous liquids should always be carried (and may be stored) in special carriers or safety containers [see 16.1].

DfEE Safety
Ch. 8

When purchasing large bottles of hazardous chemicals, schools should consider specifying the plastic-coated glass bottles offered by most suppliers.

Large cylinders containing compressed gases should always be moved on suitable trolleys. When being used or stored, these cylinders should be attached vertically to a firm support, using appropriate clamps with straps or chains, or chained on a suitable trolley [see 9.1].

Transporting hazardous substances by car may well invalidate the insurance cover. If it is necessary to move such substances by car (eg between sites) expert advice should be sought (eg from CLEAPSS or SSERC).

7.6 Spill Kits

Handbook
Ch. 7.7

Science departments are recommended to have available a general spill kit (see Table 7.1) and a special kit to deal with mercury (see Table 7.2).

---

[1] *Preparing COSHH Risk Assessments for Project Work in Schools*, (Appendix 10), SSERC, 1991

Table 7.1 *General-purpose spill kit*

Plastic dustpan and brush	Plastic scoop
Plastic bucket	Protective gloves
Eye protection	Floor cloths
Heavy-gauge polythene bags	Paper towels

Dispersing agent (eg Teepol) 1 litre
Citric acid 1.5 kg
Sodium carbonate (soda ash) 1.5 kg
Mineral absorbent (eg cat litter) 5 kg
Virkon disinfectant l litre

Table 7.2 *Mercury spill kit*

Pooter reserved for mercury	Teat pipette (or small plastic syringe)
One 2 cm paint brush	Small polythene bottle (for mercury)

Wooden lollipop sticks 10
Wooden strips 500 x 30 x 5 mm^3
Copper powder 250 g
2 M hydrochloric acid 100 cm^3
Calcium hydroxide/flowers of sulphur mixture 1 kg

Haz Man

Teachers must be fully acquainted with the properties and methods of safe handling of all substances they intend to use. During lessons involving either class practical work or demonstrations, the appropriate neutralising materials should be to hand.

Procedures for dealing with chemical spills are given in 15.9.

Spills of microorganism cultures may result in the formation of a contaminated aerosol cloud and should be dealt with using appropriate procedures [see 13.4].

7.7 Fume Cupboards

Teachers and technicians should use, and ensure that pupils use, fume cupboards whenever risk assessments require them. That is, for activities that would otherwise result in significant exposure to hazardous gases or vapours, or to small particles of irritant solids.

DfEE Safety Ch. 10

Fume cupboards, with quietly operating fan extraction, should be available for all work which requires them. With the advent of balanced science courses many teachers will need to work in rooms with fume cupboards. Whatever the initial use envisaged for a particular laboratory, the possibility of needs changing over time should be borne in mind.

Moreover, it is often forgotten how frequently hazardous chemicals are used even in the teaching of physics (eg bromine) and biology (eg formalin). Moving classes in order to provide access to a fume cupboard may be inconvenient and disruptive, and thus unlikely to happen. Mobile fume cupboards may provide a solution in some instances. Conditions will vary from school to school but in some situations up to half the laboratories may need fume cupboard provision. The need for technicians to have convenient and ready access to fume cupboards should not be overlooked.

Both the design and installation of laboratory fume cupboards should be to the standards of Design Note 29[2], including, for example, the provision for an adequate supply of "replacement air". The work should at least be supervised by a qualified ventilation engineer and reliance not placed solely on the "expertise" of architects or builders.

Topics Ch.15

Handbook Ch. 8.3

7.8   Ventilation

Extractor fans are likely to be necessary in preparation rooms or in laboratories which have low ceilings or are of below average size, especially when practical work with chemicals is undertaken. Opening windows may sometimes be of use but is not always practicable.

If the room is fitted with blackout, care should be taken to ensure that the blackout arrangements do not interfere with effective operation of the ventilation system and that the latter does not reduce the effectiveness of the former.

Ventilation fans should be fitted in addition to those in fume cupboards and care must be exercised to ensure that these fans do not interfere with the airflow for the correct working of fume cupboards. This applies particularly in laboratories that have low ceilings.

As with fume cupboards [see 7.7], professional advice should be sought on the provision, siting and efficient functioning of all forms of ventilation, including that in darkrooms, stores and preparation rooms.

Handbook Ch. 8.2

7.9   Safety Signs

Safety signs are used to give a message to people in their vicinity by the use of a combination of colour, shape, pictorial symbols and location. They may be displayed on walls, doors, stands, etc, and are subject to different regulations from those that require hazard warning symbols on bottles or equipment[3].

Safety signs need only be displayed where they are necessary to reduce hazards that cannot be completely controlled by other means[4]. However, when they are displayed, they must conform to the relevant British and International Standards.

Handbook Ch. 8.6.1

[2]   *Fume Cupboards in Schools*, DES Design Note 29, DES Architects and Building Group, 1982, ISSN 0 1412825 (Revised version in preparation 1995)

[3]   *Chemical (Hazards Information and Packaging) Regulations 1994*, HMSO, 1994 ("CHIP2 Regulations")

[4]   *Safety Signs Regulations 1994*, HMSO, 1994

The regulations recognise four categories of safety sign.

Prohibition signs indicate that certain behaviour is not permitted. The prohibited activity is symbolised in black on a white background and enclosed within a red circle with a red diagonal stripe superimposed as shown for the "No Smoking" sign in Figure 7.1. These are familiar as road signs.

Figure 7.1

Other common examples are shown in Figure 7.2.

| NO NAKED FLAMES | DO NOT EXTINGUISH WITH WATER | NOT DRINKING WATER |

Figure 7.2

Warning signs give notice of a hazard. They take the form of triangles, as illustrated in Figure 7.3 and should be in black on a yellow background. Commonly displayed signs include:

GENERAL DANGER   RISK OF FIRE   RISK OF EXPLOSION

TOXIC HAZARD   CORROSIVE SUBSTANCE   RISK OF IONISING
RADIATION

RISK OF ELECTRIC SHOCK   LASER BEAM   NON-IONISING RADIATION

BIOHAZARD

Figure 7.3

The symbols in Figure 7.3 are, where relevant, the same as the hazard
warnings used on labels. On bottles the picture will be in a square, as in the
examples in Figure 7.4. (On vehicles it will be in a diamond.)

OXIDISING   HARMFUL/IRRITANT   DANGEROUS FOR
                                                 THE ENVIRONMENT

Figure 7.4

Mandatory signs indicate that a specific course of action has to be taken. They should be white on a blue background as illustrated in Figure 7.5, which shows some of the more common signs.

EYE PROTECTION   RESPIRATORY PROTECTION   HAND PROTECTION
MUST BE WORN   MUST BE WORN   MUST BE WORN

Figure 7.5

Safe condition signs should be white on a green background as illustrated in Fig. 7.6, which shows two of the common internationally agreed signs.

FIRST AID   INDICATION OF DIRECTION

Figure 7.6

Supplementary signs may be used in which the outline is rectangular and the text is white on red for prohibition, black on yellow for warning, white on blue for mandatory information and white on green for safe conditions.

8 Apparatus Under Stress

DfEE Safety
Ch. 8.5

8.1 Handling Glass

Broken glass is a common cause of laboratory accidents. All glass items should therefore be handled and stored with care.

Bungs and stoppers should be inserted into test tubes with a slight twisting motion. When fitting safety fillers to pipettes, pupils should be taught to hold the pipette only a centimetre or so from the end, so the lever effect is minimised and breakage is less likely to occur.

DfEE Safety
Ch. 14.4

Technicians and, where relevant, teachers and older pupils, should be instructed in the appropriate methods for smoothing sharp edges of tubing (by removing sharp edges with gauze and then flame polishing) and the safe method of inserting glass tubes, rods or thermometers into bungs (see Figure 8.1). Steps (i) to (iv) below outline a safe technique, although many science departments now purchase pre-bored bungs and will only need to follow steps (iii) to (v).

(i) Choose a diameter of cork borer that is the same size as the tube, rod, or thermometer.

Figure 8.1(i)

(ii) Insert the cork borer into the bung and remove the waste plug.

Figure 8.1(ii)

(iii) Into the hole insert a cork borer of a slightly larger diameter (it should stretch the rubber so no cutting is needed).

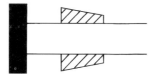

Figure 8.1(iii)

(iv) Insert the tube, rod or thermometer into the cork borer.

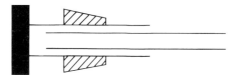

Figure 8.1(iv)

(v) Remove the cork borer.

Figure 8.1(v)

Propane-1,2,3-triol (glycerol) is a good lubricant for use with the cork borer. The glass should be held in a glove or cloth. To remove glass tubing from a bung, reverse the above procedure. It is always better to sacrifice a bung by cutting it than to struggle to remove stuck glass.

8.2   Removing Glass Stoppers

A glass-stoppered bottle should be opened with care, particularly if the stopper is tight. Stoppers stick because they are a poor fit, have been put in a warm bottle or have become cemented by some chemical.

The use of **glass** stoppers should be avoided for bottles containing sodium hydroxide and other alkaline solutions.

If the stopper is tight, the bottle should be placed in a bowl, large enough to hold the contents in case of accidents, and the stopper tapped with another glass stopper; this is more effective than tapping with anything else. Brief gentle warming of the neck of the bottle can help. If the bottle contains volatile or dangerous chemicals (particularly silicon tetrachloride – see 15.6), special care is needed and a dry cloth should be used to cover the stopper and bottle before opening.

8.3 Apparatus Under Pressure

Apparatus subjected to large pressure differences (high or low pressures) may disintegrate by explosion or implosion, so safety screens and eye protection should always be used in such situations [see Ch. 9].

Reprints
Sec. C

A completely sealed vessel should never be heated. Accidents can occur as a result of blockages that have sealed what were thought to be open vessels.

Apparatus for distillation under reduced pressure and vessels containing substances under reduced pressure (eg vacuum desiccators) should be used with eye protection and safety screens which protect both the class and the teacher. The hazards are minimised if the apparatus is carefully inspected for cracks and scratches and if spherical vessels are chosen instead of those with plane surfaces. One of the main hazards arises because of pressure differences between the inside and the outside. Even an efficient filter pump can reduce the pressure down to 2 kPa (15 mm Hg), a pressure difference of 99 kPa (743 mm Hg) and, although electrically-operated rotary pumps can reach 0.01 Pa (10^{-4} mm Hg), this only increases the pressure difference to 101 kPa (758 mm Hg).

Reprints
Sec. F

DfEE Safety
Ch. 18.1

Bell jars: only those sold for use at reduced pressure should be used for investigations involving the formation of vacuums. Other bell jars sold as covers should not be used. The bell jar should stand on a metal or glass sheet of adequate thickness; window glass should not be used.

Reprints
Sec. C

Ion exchange resins are packed dry when purchased. Water is added to the dry resin for use in schools and the increase in volume when wetted has caused explosions in confined spaces, ie glass columns. Therefore water should be added slowly and carefully, in wide containers, upon first use. The same procedure should take place on subsequent use if it is suspected that the resin has completely dried out [see 15.7].

The 'bursting bottle' experiment (ie to show the expansion of ice) can take place with considerable violence, especially if the water has been well heated to remove dissolved air. The freezing bottle must be enclosed in another container or wrapped in a cloth.

Glass gas syringes require careful maintenance, particularly in relation to the smooth movement of the plunger to ensure that they work effectively. The plunger should be attached to the barrel by wire or string to ensure that it cannot become an ejected 'missile' when high pressures develop.

8.4   Eudiometers

There is always some risk of glass shattering when gas mixtures are exploded in eudiometers. Safety screens should always be employed when a eudiometer is in use.

Eudiometers can be used safely in schools for exploding small quantities (up to 10 cm^3) of hydrogen/oxygen, hydrogen/air, or alkane/air mixtures. Hydrocarbons other than alkanes must **not** be used. **Ethyne (acetylene)** is particularly dangerous. Mixtures of hydrocarbons with **oxygen *must not*** be used in eudiometers or other glass vessels.

9 Gases Under Pressure

9.1 Gas Cylinders

Handbook
Ch. 13.3

A cylinder of compressed gas may present a significant hazard if the pressure is suddenly released. In addition, there may be a hazard dependent upon the nature of the gas itself [see Ch. 15].

Haz Man

As these cylinders contain gas under high pressure (up to 150 atmospheres, 15 MN m^{-2}), they should be stored in a cool place. They must never be left to roll around freely, but should be chained or clamped firmly, in an upright position, or used in the special stands available. For transporting the cylinders, the use of special trolleys is recommended.

The Health and Safety Executive defines the following three categories for heeping gas cylinders but only the last two of these apply to schools:

- storage (ie outside, for large numbers of cylinders)
- holding, and about to use
- holding and using

Care should be taken to ensure that all valves are clean, dry and free from grease. Glass-working torches should be fitted with non-return valves in the fuel and air/oxygen lines. Considerable damage has been caused by not observing this procedure.

The ignition of hydrogen/air mixtures is the commonest source of serious explosions in school laboratories. While not free from risk, cylinders of compressed hydrogen gas provide a safer source of hydrogen than most school methods of generating the gas; not only is the hydrogen likely to be purer, but the rate of flow can be closely controlled. The relatively high rates of flow available mean that air can be more readily flushed through apparatus. Hydrogen cylinders should, however, be fitted with a needle valve to control the flow of gas as well as a pressure-reducing valve.

Reprints
Sec. C

While it is usually appreciated that a leak of hydrogen into the atmosphere may cause an explosion, this is not very likely because of the speed at which the gas diffuses. However, the serious fire hazard arising from a leak of oxygen is less well known. In an atmosphere containing as little as 25% oxygen, materials ignite at much lower temperatures than normal and burn furiously [see also 15.5].

Gas cylinders will be checked for leaks by the supplier when being refilled. Schools should check gas cylinder regulators annually for leaks using detergent solution (there is no requirement to inspect gas cylinder regulators against a written scheme). They should be checked every five years by a specialist company.

9.2 Autoclaves, Pressure Cookers and Model Steam Engines

Autoclaves and pressure cookers can be dangerous unless properly used and serviced. Operators should be adequately trained in their use.

Handbook
Ch. 15.12

In using an autoclave or pressure cooker, care should be taken to ensure that[1]:

Topics Ch. 5

- it is filled with sufficient water,
- only distilled or deionised water is used,
- it is never overloaded,
- openings to the pressure-release valve are not obstructed,
- bottles containing media for sterilisation have their caps loosened before autoclaving (or microwaving),
- all the air is expelled from the autoclave before the steam vent is closed,
- the pressure for which the apparatus was designed is never exceeded,
- after use, the pressure is allowed to fall slowly to atmospheric before opening (do not rely on the accuracy of a fitted pressure gauge),
- heat-resistant gloves are worn when unloading,
- an autoclave is never left with water in it for any length of time as this will accelerate metal corrosion.

DfEE Safety
Ch. 8.6

SSERC 182

Reprints
Sec. F

Regular inspection of autoclaves and pressure cookers is required under the *Pressure Systems and Transportable Gas Containers Regulations.* It is the responsibility of the employer to make arrangements for these inspections. The services of an insurance company may be used or the inspections may be delegated to competent persons in schools (eg a science teacher or technician). A suitable written scheme is needed for the periodic examinations, and this will specify how freqently examinations are to be carried out. Examination involves checking for signs of physical damage, the normal operation of the pressure-release valve and whether any rubber seal is flexible and in good condition.

DfEE Safety
Ch. 18.1

Before attempting to use a model steam engine, check that its pressure-release valve operates freely [see 10.3]. Regular inspection is required using a suitable written scheme for periodic examination, as discussed above.

9.3 Generation of Gases

Reprints
Sec. C

High pressure may develop in apparatus in which gases are generated. Many accidents in schools are caused by blockages in such apparatus. A check should be carried out on the free flow of air through apparatus before adding any chemicals.

Reprints
Sec. C

Gas-generating reactions, including fermentations, must never be carried out in sealed vessels.

---

[1] Schools in Scotland should consult the Strathclyde *Approved Code of Practice*

This is particularly important with the increased use of fermenters as part of a biotechnology course, where comparatively large volumes of liquid (and therefore gas) may be involved [see 13.3].

There is no objection to the use of pressure-release valves (eg air locks and Bunsen valves) but care must be taken to ensure that the valves work freely.

Some practical situations which have, in the past, led to accidents as a result of pressure build up within apparatus include:

Reprints
Sec. C

- the use of Bunsen valves made from rubber tubing which is old and inflexible or too thick,
- the reaction between sulphur dioxide and oxygen in which crystals of sulphur(VI) oxide may block the delivery tube,
- the thermal decomposition of plastics in which liquid products may condense in, and block, the delivery tube,
- blocked drying towers or U-tubes containing old 'anhydrous" calcium chloride or other drying solid,
- the recharging of a lead-acid storage battery in which gases produced are not able to escape, or shorting or attempting to charge lithium cells.

Reprints
Sec. D

9.4 Explosions

A number of demonstrations in science teaching involve controlled explosions. Pupils often find such lessons particularly memorable and they have a legitimate place in school science when they are justified by the content of what is being taught. These activities are safe providing risk assessments have taken place and the appropriate procedures adopted.

The demonstration of the explosion of custard powder or lycopodium powder (in a can) should use 250–500 cm^3 sized cans only and have safety screens in place for both pupils and the teacher in addition to the use of eye protection. As an added precaution pupils should be a safe distance away (2–3 m).

Reprints
Sec. C

The same procedures should be adopted for demonstrating the explosion of a methane/air mixture (to illustrate internal combustion).

A very small amount (one drop) of petroleum ether (40–60) can be safely exploded in a 20 cm^3 plastic syringe of oxygen. Use safety screens and keep at a safe distance as above, with the added precautions:

SSERC 148

- keep the fuel container closed when not in use and well away from any naked flame
- use only small dispensing containers to minimise fire risk
- do not pump the oxygen syringe back and forth as there is potential for the non-return valve to fill with an explosive mixture of oxygen and fuel
- do not use an oxygen cylinder without a needle (pressure-reducing) valve
- clamp the cylinder to a bench or trolley.

Mixtures of hydrogen and oxygen can be safely exploded, for example in small 300 cm^3) plastic wash bottles. The bottle should be filled with water, and the hydrogen and oxygen bubbled in from cylinders, or be generated by a method which does not require heating. Larger volumes can be exploded out of doors, but the noise is **very** loud, and there is some risk of damage to the ear unless both teacher and spectators are a considerable distance away (at least 10 m, preferably more), or wear hearing protectors.

10 Mechanical Hazards

10.1 Centrifuges

Centrifuges used in schools are very low powered in comparison, for example, with those used in medical research. In many cases there should now be an interlock on the lid to prevent it being opened until the rotor has stopped as required by the latest British Standard *BS 7687, 1993*. Although this cannot be applied to existing school centrifuges, when a new model is purchased it should comply with the relevant provision of this Standard. Moreover, the HSE expects employers to have a policy of progressive replacement of old models with newer and safer types.

DfEE Safety Ch. 8.1

SSERC 182

There is no need for an interlock on many small bench models but the requirements for this exemption are complex and details should be sought from CLEAPSS or SSERC. At present schools are not required to buy any particular type of centrifuge but if a European Product Directive on centrifuges is produced a school would only be able to purchase one with a CE mark. Under the *Provision and Use of Work Equipment Regulations* the centrifuge must be "safe and suitable" for its intended use. If one is bought which does not meet *BS 7687* the supplier should indicate whether it is safe and suitable for school use. The Regulations become fully applicable in January 1997 at which time all existing equipment will need to comply with them. In any case the centrifuge must be electrically safe and installed and operated according to the manufacturer's instructions.

DfEE Safety Ch. 18.1

Handbook Ch. 12.4

SSERC 132

10.2 Air Pistols and Air Rifles

The apparatus used in physics to illustrate the principle of conservation of momentum and to help refine the concept of speed using a mounted air pistol or air rifle, is safe as long as it is used correctly.

The following rules should be followed to ensure safety.

- The alignment of the pistol or rifle should not be adjusted except by the manufacturer.
- The apparatus should be supported on a rigid laboratory bench and clamped, as necessary, to ensure correct alignment is maintained.
- All present should be wearing eye protection and keep behind the muzzle of the gun when it is fired.

- A suitable backstop should be provided to catch the pellet, eg a metal waste bin lined with felt or foam.
- The backstop should be screened on both sides with safety screens.
- A teacher unfamiliar with this procedure should receive training before demonstrating it to a class.

10.3 Steam Engines

DfEE Safety
Ch. 18.1

Handbook
Ch. 10.5

SSERC 182

All model steam engines should be fitted with a safety valve on the boiler; boilers have exploded when the safety valve became stuck. Before use, teachers should check that the valve is in working order by moving the spring-loaded ball or plunger by hand [see also 4.4, 9.2 and 6.1].

Solid fuel [see 6.2] should be used rather than liquid (methylated spirits) or liquid petroleum gas. Liquid fuel, often in a plastic bottle, has been the cause of several serious accidents. The solid fuel (probably Meta fuel or hexamine) needs to be handled with care. It is particularly important to avoid skin contact and it is better if the fuel does not have to be broken into small pieces. The fumes from burning fuel should also be avoided but typical laboratory ventilation will ensure minimal exposure. The fumes from solid fuel are worse if the fuel has to be extinguished rather than the fuel being allowed to burn itself out. If the extinguished fuel, still in its holder, is put in a can with a tight-fitting lid this will reduce the fume problem considerably.

Steam engines are subject to the *Pressure Systems Regulations* and so need regular inspections [see 9.2]. Technicians, given suitable guidance, would be competent to carry this out unless an employer decides otherwise. Steam engines intended for use by adults may have higher operating and release valve pressures than those intended for use by children. Such engines should be restricted solely to teacher demonstration.

10.4 Heavy Masses

Handbook
Ch. 12.1

DfEE Safety
Ch. 8.4

DfEE Safety
Ch. 18.1

The task of transporting heavy masses (eg gas cylinders, trolley runways) has implications for science staff, especially technicians, and is subject to clear control by legislation through the *Manual Handling Regulations*.

Some practical work in physics requires the use of masses up to 20 kg. In many cases these masses are suspended by wires or pulley systems. Care should be taken to prevent feet or hands straying into the danger zone by placing a cardboard box full of waste packing material directly below the suspended mass [see 10.6].

10.5 Tools and Model Making

DfEE Safety
Ch. 16.1

DfEE Safety
Ch. 8.1

Technological activities frequently involve the use of tools not traditionally used in science laboratories [see 11.10].

The use of power tools should be subject to severe restriction. The suitability of resources for use in schools from DIY and similar outlets must be viewed with caution. The *Work Equipment Regulations* require that such resources must be safe for use in schools and high street retailers do not cater specifically for such a market [see 2.2].

> It may be advisable to equip one corner of a laboratory with a vice, bench hook or other means of holding wood or metal while it is sawn or drilled. Generally power tools should not be available for pupils to use but there are model-making tools for shaping, cutting and drilling which may be allowed. Risk assessments carried out on the intended activity will determine which tools are acceptable.
>
> Other activities call for the use of sharp craft knives which may present problems of discipline and require instruction to be given in their proper use. Razor blades used to make narrow slits for optics work require great care in handling and storage.

DfEE Safety
Ch. 18.1

10.6 Wires Under Tension

When a wire or nylon filament is under tension considerable amounts of energy can be stored in it.

Handbook
Ch. 12.1

> Should the wire break or the anchorage fail, the wire may whip round on the users who should therefore be wearing appropriate eye protection [see 7.1].

10.7 Tamper Proofing

Mechanical locking is quite frequently provided on the controls of school laboratory equipment. The usefulness of locking devices disappears if pupils gain access to the "keys" used or can circumvent the locks because of inadequate design.

> In the case of low-voltage power supplies, inadequate locking may result in the loss of a few lamp bulbs or other components. In a more serious incident, however, the failure of a lock on a thermostat control resulted in the explosion of the containers being incubated in a dual-purpose incubator/oven because their contents were boiled. The oven was destroyed. There is another lesson to learn from this incident: cultures being incubated should not be in air-tight containers.

11 Electricity

11.1 Mains Installations

Reprints
Sec. D

Teaching pupils about the hazards of mains electricity should form part of all science courses.

The HSE has issued specific guidance on electrical safety in schools.[1]

Fixed electrical installations, including mains socket outlets, should be inspected and tested periodically by a qualified electrician.

Handbook
Ch. 6.5

Teachers or technicians could use a simple proprietary tester such as the "Check Plug" to identify some major faults. The frequency at which professional checks are required depends on the environment (eg the presence of corrosive vapours), the age of the installation and the amount of rough usage. The electrical system used in rooms where water is splashed about during washing or where the humidity is very high, such as animal houses or greenhouses, will have to be fitted with either waterproof socket outlets or other forms of protection.

Any modifications or extensions to mains circuits must be to safe, ie professional, standards. This is a statutory requirement arising from the *Electricity at Work Regulations* with the standards set by the *IEE Wiring Regulations*. Earth leakage circuit breakers (ELCBs) which also include Residual Current Devices (RCDs) are often used in the belief that they prevent electric shock. They do not, but do reduce the severity of the shock by disconnecting the supply very quickly. This protection is available if the fault path is between live and earth. However, if any part of the body forms a current pathway between "live" and "neutral" these devices will **not** operate to cut off the supply unless there is also a pathway from "live" to "earth". A current passing to "earth" is required to make them operate. Even then, in the time taken for the current to earth to reach the required tripping value, the current through the body could have caused lethal damage. For the protection of people RCDs with a sensitivity no greater than 30 mA should be used.

---

[1] *Electrical Safety in Schools, Guidance Note GS23*, HSE, 1990

SSERC 185

Particular care should be taken over temporary modifications for "open days", etc, with no relaxation of safety standards. It is now impracticable to use water pipes as earth connections since continuity is often broken by plastic sections. Great care must be exercised, and extra precautions are necessary, when temporary extension leads are used especially if they take power supplies outdoors. While RCDs may give some protection note the limitations mentioned above. Pupils should never be allowed to install temporary extensions of power supplies.

DfEE Safety
Ch. 5.2, 6.2

SSERC 181

All science staff should be able to take immediate emergency action in cases of electric shock [see 17.3]. A means of cutting off the mains electricity supply should be provided in each laboratory and science staff should know its location and be trained in its use. In-house training should be part of the induction process for new staff. The use of signs indicating the location of mains cut-off switches is strongly recommended.

Over the next few years the rating plate fixed to electrical equipment will indicate "230 V ac" instead of "240 V ac". This is part of European Union harmonisation and is a nominal change for England, Scotland and Wales, no change for Northern Ireland and a move up from 220 V ac for the rest of the EU. In terms of safety the change is insignificant; the hazard of "230 V ac" remains the same. Equipment performance is mostly unaffected.

Reprints
Sec. D

SSERC 181

Some new and recently re-wired laboratories may be fitted with mains sockets that no longer have shutters operated by the insertion of the earth pin. Instead, they operate when live and neutral shutters are simultaneously depressed with a minimum force of 5 N. Accidents have been reported when pupils have mistakenly inserted two 4 mm connectors simultaneously into the live and neutral apertures. If disabled 13 A plugs are used in the teaching of plug wiring, it is imperative to check that they will not fit into these new style shuttered sockets otherwise the result could be fatal. This is another instance where an ELCB (RCD) might give little or no protection against a severe electric shock.

11.2 Mains Driven Equipment

SSERC 184

Handbook
Ch. 6.5

Many portable mains-operated items of equipment must be inspected at least once a term and tested by a competent person at least once a year and a record kept. Some portable items which are moved only occasionally may need less frequent inspection. The competent person need not be a qualified electrician – it may be a teacher or technician with suitable technical expertise, especially one who has been on a training course for this purpose. It is the employer's responsibility to determine the arrangements. Some insurers refuse to accept "in-house" inspection in the belief that economic pressure may be exerted on the tester to pass items which would otherwise fail.

All equipment with a mains plug on its supply lead should be considered.

Inspection can reveal:

Reprints
Sec. D

- loose connections,
- damaged plugs,
- "frayed" or damaged leads,
- inappropriate fuses,
- loose or damaged casings on equipment,
- signs of over-heating.

Electrical tests would reveal:

- inadequate earth connections except on double-insulated equipment where no earth is required,
- insulation faults.

Handbook
Ch. 6.4

Audio-visual equipment, computers, VDUs and balances present particular problems; earthing tests should only be carried out on the frame, not on moving parts nor on components which are earthed only for electrical screening. If in doubt, the manufacturer should be consulted before testing. In rare cases some tests may be omitted and the inspection made specially thorough.

DfEE Safety
Ch. 8.1

SSERC 180

A certain standard of quality and suitability is expected from manufacturers of products for school use. European legislation is beginning to affect schools in respect of what is considered suitable [see 2.2].

Reprints Sec.D

SSERC 172

The number of glue guns which develop electrical faults is a cause for concern and these items deserve special attention during inspection and testing. For all equipment it is a requirement to use 3-pin plugs with sleeved pins (which all new plugs have) when replacement is necessary. Old plugs with unsleeved pins should not be reused. The 13 A fuse usually found in new plugs is often too highly rated and if so should be replaced with one of a lower rating to suit the equipment.

11.3 Live Working and High Voltages

SSERC 172,
173, 184

No-one, neither pupils nor staff, should normally be allowed to work on equipment with exposed mains connections. Staff would need to be trained, facilities must be suitable and extra precautions taken if such work is to be considered. Statutory requirements must be adhered to [see 11.1].

Low-voltage (25 V or less) live working is generally safe. A few items of laboratory electrical equipment have accessible socket outlets classed as "hazardous live". This expression means that touching the outlet could give rise to a harmful electrical shock. Whether the outlet is "hazardous live" will depend on voltage, current, capacitance and environmental conditions. For indoor dry conditions voltages above 30 V ac (60 V dc) are called "hazardous live". However, in schools, 25 V ac or dc is usually regarded as the safe maximum. Even senior students under close supervision should only be allowed to use equipment which has parts at more than 25 V if special precautions are taken and following proper instruction. Shrouded plugs should be used.

Reprints
Sec. D

SSERC 173

A normal, healthy person is unlikely to be harmed by a current of 5 mA, or less, flowing through the body via skin contacts. However, since the resistance of the skin varies widely, it is difficult to calculate a voltage which is low enough to keep the current to a safe value under all conditions. In any situation, a lower voltage is safer than a higher one, but a normal, healthy person is unlikely to receive a harmful electric shock from a source giving no more than 40 V. An ordinary ac source of 30 V rms will have a peak value of over 40 V and this is one reason hazardous live working has a lower limit for ac than for dc.

The *Electricity at Work Regulations* require that facilities for maintenance and fault-finding work involving hazardous live should provide for the best possible safeguards for technical staff. These facilities would include, for example, an isolating transformer supplying sockets on a work bench and posters illustrating the treatment of persons suffering from electric shock prominently displayed[2]. Generally, as such facilities are not provided in schools, such work should not be attempted.

Staff may carry out repairs to mains-powered equipment only if permitted to do so by their employer. Such equipment should be made dead before work commences.

Topics Ch. 3

Handbook
Ch. 12.9.6

SSERC 158

DfEE Safety
Ch. 16.1

Reprints Sec.D

Teachers must consult appropriate risk assessments before carrying out demonstrations (such as the conductivity of hot glass) using exposed mains connections. They should adhere not only to the safety precautions required, for example making it impossible to touch exposed connectors, but also stress the need for them to their pupils. Similar precautions are needed when using any exposed supply designated as hazardous live.

The transmission line demonstration has produced so many accidents over the years that it deserves special consideration of how it should be performed to avoid, as far as possible, the risk of electric shock.

Some employers may recommend a limit of 30 V ac for the transmission line but if a higher voltage is used all high-voltage wires and components must be insulated or completely enclosed to prevent inadvertent contact.

Isolating transformers are often used but not all transformers are of this type. Residual current devices (RCDs) are also available in plug tops and adaptors and may be used but should never be the only means of protection; the lack of protection they provide when live to neutral electric shocks are a likely hazard has already been noted [see 11.1]. RCDs will give no protection against shocks in a typical high voltage transmission line demonstration because there is no connection between the mains and the actual transmission line.

DfEE Safety
Ch. 8.3

A teacher unfamiliar with demonstrations involving exposed mains connections must receive training before carrying them out. This training may be school based or part of a new science teacher's induction programme.

High Tension (HT) means voltages between 25 V to 400 V and a

---

[2]   *Electrical Safety in Schools, Guidance Note GS23*, HSE, 1990

current which may be greater than 5 mA. Extra High Tension (EHT) can be any voltage over 25 V but is usually over 400 V with the current strictly limited to less than 5 mA. No pupil should use supplies with more than 25 V on open terminals or with uninsulated conductors. Older students using HT supplies, or in any hazardous live situation, should use shrouded 4 mm plug leads for any connection which may be broken while the power is on, although safe practice should not allow this.

> All work with a supply capable of delivering currents greater than 5 mA at high voltage should be done as teacher demonstrations for pupils up to Y11 (or S4 in Scotland). In the sixth form students may be allowed to use HT but only after careful instruction as to how the risks are reduced and under close supervision. Power supply units with both HT (eg between 40 and 400 V) and LT (or LV) outputs may introduce unacceptable hazards. Disabling the HT output by removing the appropriate fuse to enable the LT (or LV) output to be used by pupils does little to reduce the hazard because a fuse is so easily replaced or circumvented with metal foil, a paper clip, etc. If in doubt do not allow pupils access to such units.

EHT supply units suitable for school use should have a maximum output current of 5 mA.

> Special care should be taken with apparatus (such as that from government surplus or ordinary retail outlets) which has not been designed primarily for school use: the best advice is not to use it. Be careful with electrostatic generators with large capacitors — the initial discharge current may approach safe limits. However, the induction coils and van de Graaff generators now used in schools can only supply currents much lower than 5 mA [see 12.7]. Very old induction coils may produce much larger currents and so should not be used.

Reprints
Sec. D

The most common source of EHT in most laboratories is the TV set. Some older sets modified for use as oscilloscopes (eg to show Lissajou's figures) will probably fail to satisfy modern safety requirements.

> Exposure to electric shock hazard has also arisen from a TV set modified to prevent theft, eg by having a metal chain or strap bolted to the frame. This should only be done by a competent person after advice from the manufacturers.

Reprints
Sec. E

Electrophoresis investigations, for example the separation of DNA components using supplies at more than 25 V dc, should only use apparatus designed with an interlock to prevent the possibility of shocks. The apparatus now available to schools for doing practical work on DNA is normally restricted to low voltages by the use of plug-top adaptors or dry cells.

> These investigations may be particularly hazardous if DIY installations are employed because of the possible proximity of high voltages and conducting solutions. For this reason schools should use only commercially available versions and not attempt to produce their own.

11.4 Flammable Atmospheres

Haz Man

Electrical equipment which may operate in flammable atmospheres must have spark-free, or flame-proof, switchgear and any heating elements must be sealed. It is particularly important that this equipment is constructed to British Standards specifications which means it should come from a specialist supplier and cannot be a DIY installation.

> The light switch inside a chemical store in which flammables are kept would need to be of such specialist construction but only if the flammables were dispensed or decanted within the store. The lights are often operated from ordinary switches which should be fitted outside the store.

SSERC 172

> Flammable liquids and biological preparations with flammable vapours must not be stored in domestic refrigerators; the light and thermostat switches have been known to ignite such vapours with disastrous consequences.

11.5 Aquaria

Handbook
Ch. 14.3

The combination of mains electricity and impure water presents particular and possibly severe hazards. Aquarium accessories should be of a design which conforms to current electrical safety regulations and should be installed in a safe, professional manner.

11.6 Body Monitoring

DfEE Safety
Ch. 16.1,
17.5

SSERC 185

Practical work in which electrodes contact the body must use the lowest possible voltages both in powering amplifiers and in stimulation. Purpose built bio-amplifiers properly connected will ensure the dc voltage used is as low as possible (ac is not permitted) and will use some form of isolation between the electrodes and any mains-powered apparatus. It is unlikely that any DIY system would be as safe and such set-ups cannot be recommended [see 14.5].

Handbook
Ch. 11.8.3.

> Skin resistance provides the major safeguard in reducing the severity of electric shock. However, body monitoring activities use contacts designed to minimise this resistance. Mains-powered ancillary equipment (eg oscilloscopes, chart recorders, etc.) must not therefore be directly connected to the body-monitoring circuitry except through opto-isolation or similar systems.

11.7 Rechargeable Cells and Capacitors

Handbook
Ch. 9.3

SSERC 185

Lead-acid accumulators and NiFe (nickel-iron) cells have been used in school laboratories for many years. The correct procedures for charging and handling the electrolytes should be followed. Charging lead-acid cells will produce hydrogen and oxygen which can lead to violent explosions when venting has been overlooked or sparks are produced on connection or disconnection. These hazards can even occur with the smaller cells designed for pupil use. Small NiCad (nickel-cadmium) cells are being used to an increasing extent and the correct procedures for recharging and use should be followed. Detailed instructions are always supplied with the cells or charging units.

Reprints
Sec. D

For maximum life NiCad cells must be charged at a constant current and so a constant voltage supply (eg a normal LV power unit) is not suitable without a special regulator circuit. Rechargers designed for such use are often more convenient than DIY circuits. The use of rapid recharging is inappropriate for schools unless the time of charge can be accurately controlled; it can cause overheating and probably reduces the life of the cells.

If sealed lead-acid cells are used they must not be treated in the same way as NiCad cells. The manufacturer's instructions must be followed in respect of charging and safe storage. Attempts to recharge other types of dry cells are hazardous except with specially designed equipment and the appropriate cells. Pupils should not be allowed to recharge cells.

The low internal resistance of NiCad and similar cells can lead to a rapid discharge if they are short circuited. They may get hot enough to melt plastic holders and surprise the unwary. This has implications for safe storage of such cells. NiCad cells of poor quality have been known to rupture as a result of being short circuited.

Lithium cells are unlikely to be used in schools because of their cost but they may be found fitted in some equipment. They are quite unsuitable for use outside such equipment because they can explode with great violence if used incorrectly.

Capacitors (condensers) are often ignored when electric shock and other hazards are considered. Large capacitors can store sufficient charge to give an unpleasant electric shock which, although doing little direct damage, may lead to serious injury through involuntary movement.

Electrolytic capacitors can explode if misused. This misuse can arise from:

Handbook
Ch. 12.5

- applying a higher voltage than the rated value
- connecting the capacitor with the wrong polarity
- a current overload
- using a capacitor which has not been used for some time and needs 're-forming'.

11.8 Radiant Heaters

SSERC 173

Mains heaters have been used as sources of heat radiation for many years. They are no longer regarded as safe because access to the element, even through a fine wire mesh cage, is easy. The mains version should now be withdrawn from use and replaced by a low-voltage model.

11.9 Power Tools

DfEE Safety
Ch. 16.1

The use of mains-powered electric drills, saws and sanders with very few exceptions should be restricted to teachers and technicians [see 10.4]. Electric shock hazards caused by cutting cables or handling with wet hands might be overlooked because the mechanical hazards are so obvious.

The use of eye protection and machine guards is expected and dust hazards should be considered. Work requiring mounted power tools (eg circular saws) should be left to trained workshop personnel.

Handbook
Ch. 11.5,
11.11

Glue guns and soldering irons are a frequent cause of minor burns and are often found to have damaged cables.

SSERC 172

Low-temperature glue guns may be considered. Poor quality models should be avoided. Soldering irons operating at 12 V or 24 V are recommended for pupil use, and heat-resistant cable will give the connecting lead a longer life.

Reprints
Sec. E

Fumes from the flux in cored solder are a known respiratory sensitiser [see 4.4, 15.2].

SSERC 186

Asthma sufferers are at particular risk and the use of rosin-free flux is now recommended especially when a lot of soldering is done, eg by a technician.

12 Radiation Hazards

12.1 Stroboscopes and Signal Generators

DfEE Safety
Ch. 17.5

Handbook
Ch. 11.8.3

Sensory stimulation at particular frequencies can have unforeseen and unpleasant physiological effects [see 11.6 and 14.5].

A frequency of 7 Hz is often considered dangerous, but the important frequencies may be within the range 4 Hz to 15 Hz or even higher. The use of sounds pulsating at such frequencies should be avoided. A signal generator driving a loudspeaker has been known to produce unpleasant feelings, even nausea, in susceptible individuals at a variety of frequencies – even above the upper threshold of hearing.

The HSE recommend that flashing lights should be kept to frequencies at or below 4 Hz, although the occurrence of photosensitive epilepsy is very rare. However anyone known to suffer from this problem should not be subjected to flickering lights. Flashing lights may also adversely affect those prone to migraine attacks.

12.2 Microwaves

Microwaves can heat and damage internal organs with very little sensory warning. Persons fitted with heart pacemakers (or other implants) should not operate microwave equipment and should consult their specialist before entering a room in which such equipment is being operated. Particular care may be needed on "open days", including the use of warning notices, etc.

Microwave transmitters designed for school laboratory use are of too low a power to present a significant risk to normal healthy individuals. Nevertheless, it would be sensible to limit the use of microwave transmitters to ensure minimum exposure. This is particularly important with more advanced microwave transmitters, for example, those used in telecommunications courses. The simplest means of doing this is not to be too close to, and not to be in line with, the beams, transmitting apertures, etc. Microwave ovens do present a risk in terms of their power output but the interlock between door and power supply would have to be circumvented or the door screen removed for the risk to be anything other than negligible. Microwave ovens bought for use in schools must comply with the relevant British Standards and must be maintained according to the manufacturer's recommendations.

Anybody with active implants, not just pacemakers, could be affected by powerful magnets or induced magnetic fields. Staff should be proactive in identifying and safeguarding persons potentially at risk. However, in schools the risk is minimal because magnetic field strengths are so low.

12.3 Radiant Heaters

Handbook
Ch. 11.9.2

Sources of heat operated at temperatures low enough for minimal visible output can produce enough radiation to cause skin burns or set combustible materials on fire.

SSERC 173

Teachers should ensure that papers are not left on the bench near to the infra-red lamps sometimes used in chemistry, nor near the radiant heaters used in physics. Investigations in which the skin is used as a detector of radiation should be carried out with care to avoid over-exposure [see 6.2, 11.8 and 12.5].

12.4 Lasers

Handbook
Ch. 12.12

The beams of some school lasers can damage the retina of the eye. The classification attached to a laser (product) indicates the relative hazard of the output from the device. Unclassified lasers should not be used in schools. If a school has an unclassified laser staff should find out what hazards it presents by reference to CLEAPSS, SSERC, the original supplier, or the manufacturer.

SSERC 185

Class 1 lasers are totally enclosed (eg a laser printer), and are safe under the conditions of intended use. Class 2 lasers are so bright that the aversion response, eg blinking, makes them safe to use. Class 3A lasers are no more hazardous unless the beam is concentrated by a lens or optical system. Class 3B lasers are always hazardous when viewed directly. Class 4 lasers should never be used in schools and the degree of control needed with class 3B makes them generally unsuitable. Only lasers up to and including Class 2 are now recommended for use in schools. Existing Class 3A lasers could continue in use with care until they can be replaced.

Pupils should be instructed not to look along the line of a laser beam of any Class and care should be taken to ensure that beams cannot be reflected into the eye at full intensity. The aversion response (blinking, etc) should not be over-ridden or ignored.

DfEE Safety
Ch. 18.1

In Scotland the latest advice on lasers is contained in SOED *Circular 7/95*[1]. Guidance given by the DES in *Administrative Memorandum 7/70* has been superseded although much of the advice is excellent in terms of good practice.

---

[1] *Use of Lasers in Laboratory Work in Schools and Colleges of Education and in Non-advanced Work in Further Education Establishments, Circular 7/95*, SOED, 1995

Goggles are **not** needed with Class 2 lasers because the power output and beam characteristics are such that they will not damage the eye. Indeed wearing laser goggles with Class 2 lasers may be hazardous because vision is so restricted.

12.5 The Sun

Handbook
Ch. 11.9.1

The focused rays of the Sun can damage the retina and people have been blinded. Exposure to solar radiation may cause skin cancer [see 12.6].

Eclipses of the Sun regularly give rise to serious accidents. Pupils should be warned never to look at the Sun directly through a filter, pinhole, lens or optical instrument. The only safe way to observe the Sun is to project its image on to a non-combustible screen.

When using daylight illumination microscopes, it should be ensured that it is impossible for the Sun to be focused through the instrument, preferably by using windows facing away from the Sun.

SSERC 181

Over-head projectors as well as round flasks, bottles, beakers etc. containing liquids, should not be left on window sills where their focusing effects on sunlight could start a fire.

12.6 Ultraviolet Radiation

Handbook
Ch. 11.9.3

It is now thought that ultraviolet radiation of any wavelength may cause skin cancer. Ultraviolet radiation of sufficiently short wavelength causes "sun burn" and can cause permanent damage to the eyes.

Handbook
Ch. 12.9.6

Lamps emitting short-wave UV (ie 315 nm or less) have clear quartz envelopes and should only be used where direct radiation is screened from the eyes by a sheet of glass or an opaque material. Lamps with dark glass envelopes emit so little of the dangerous wavelengths that the risks to the eyes are minimal but continued or repeated exposure may induce melanoma.

Arcs, whether struck between carbon or metal electrodes, are prolific sources of UV. Their use should be avoided in schools, but glass screens (at least 6 mm thick) can be used if arcs are necessary. The short exposure times likely in science lessons present little risk of melanoma.

Exposure to ultraviolet radiation from the Sun without protection for the skin is now considered to be a more serious health hazard because of the rising incidence of skin cancer.

Children working outside or on field trips and visits should now be encouraged to use lotions or creams which block UV-A (long wave) and UV-B (short wave). They should be advised not to sunbathe without adequate protection. Over-exposure to UV in childhood is thought to increase the risk of melanoma in later life.

12.7 X-Rays

DfEE Safety
Ch. 18.1

High doses of X-rays give rise to "radiation burns" and even low doses may cause malignant growths. The body should be exposed to X-radiation only when the benefit outweighs the risk, as is the case with medical applications.

Handbook
Ch. 12.10.4

X-rays are produced in low-pressure systems by sparks and discharges operating at more than 6 kV. Schools wishing to use or purchase such equipment (other than television sets) working at potentials greater than 5 kV must comply with the provisions of DES *Administrative Memorandum 1/ 92,* (in Scotland, SOED *Circular 1166*) which requires formal application and authorisation. Independent schools and incorporated colleges should seek exemption [see 12.8].

Induction coils can produce high voltages at significant power levels: a 25 mm spark between points indicates a likely potential of 30 kV. Low pressure discharge tubes connected to induction coils can produce X-rays and should not be used in this way. School electrostatic generators (van de Graaff or Wimshurst machines) operate at power levels low enough to present little risk.

12.8 Radioactivity

Radioactive substances emit ionising radiation which presents similar hazards to X-rays. Using radioactive materials introduces additional complications in that the source of radiation may be ingested, stolen, lost or damaged.

DfEE Safety
Ch. 18.1

Reprints
Sec. F

The use of radioactive substances other than those of very low specific activity (eg potassium compounds and some cloud chamber sources) is now controlled by the *Ionising Radiation Regulations* which formed the basis of DES/WO *AM 1/92,* the current official guidance for schools. In Scotland the equivalent advice is to be found in SOED *Circular 1166 (1987).* Work in schools is divided into three categories, A, B and C in which C has the lowest level of restriction and will be the category in which most schools operate. Thorium compounds are entirely prohibited in Category C work in Scotland; elsewhere they are allowed within thoron generators.

AM 1/92 does not apply to independent schools or incorporated colleges. Instead, they either need to register with HM Inspectorate of Pollution, a lengthy, formal and expensive business or claim exemption under the *Radioactive Substances (Schools etc.) Exemption Order* which is nearly always easy and costs nothing.

Handbook
Ch. 12.10

Each employer has to appoint a competent person to advise on work with ionising radiation. The employer may designate this person a Radiation Protection Adviser (RPA) and this could be the science adviser in a local authority.

Reprints
Sec. F

One or more Radiation Protection Supervisors (RPS) must be nominated in each school. Their job is to see that local rules (approved by a competent person or the RPA) are enforced. This task would normally be done by the

Head of the Department which uses the radioactive sources.

The inspection, storage and use of sources, including testing for leaks, has to be regulated with accurate record-keeping including a log book.

Uranium compounds, even if only used as chemical reagents, must now be stored in the same way as other radioactive sources and the total amount stored is restricted to a maximum of 100 g. In Scotland, uranium compounds are prohibited in Category C establishments except in the production of protactinium generators. The *Exemption Order* allows up to 2 kg of uranium and thorium compounds.

Where classes include pupils under 16, work with radioactive sources is confined to teacher demonstration except where the sources have very low specific activity as is the case with those in cloud chambers.

Reprints
Sec. F

Competency is necessary for Category C work; further training is needed for all other Categories. Teachers with science degrees or science teaching qualifications are considered "competent" for Category C work but in-house training is a good idea and employers may require that there be some formal training.

Topics Ch.13

If disposal is necessary, strict precautions must be taken. If these are followed small amounts of thorium and uranium compounds may be disposed of via ordinary waste water drains. Sealed sources may be disposed of only via the National Disposal Service which is at present provided by Safeguard International[2].

---

[2] Safeguard International Ltd, Building C2, Culham Laboratory, Abingdon, Oxfordshire, OX14 3EB. Telephone 01235 463610, Fax 01480 496801

13 Biological Hazards

13.1 General Principles

Many of the hazards associated with the use of living organisms and material of living origin are also encountered in everyday life; they include infection, allergic reactions and poisoning. Work with biological materials in science activities should not expose staff or pupils to risks which add significantly to the "burden" on the body already imposed by normal daily living. The acquisition of good habits of laboratory practice [see Ch. 4] and hygiene is of prime importance. All hand-to-mouth activities should be avoided in laboratories and nothing should be eaten or tasted unless exceptional steps have been taken to guarantee hygiene and prevent contamination of any materials used. Many of the chemicals employed in the teaching of biology are hazardous but, if prepared in schools, may not carry a warning label [see Ch. 15]. Work with animals and plants must also not infringe legal duties[1].

13.2 Microbiology

All teachers doing work with microorganisms should acquaint themselves with the risks involved, particularly of infection, which may arise both directly and as a result of the formation of aerosols. These are produced whenever the surface of a liquid is disturbed or a vessel under pressure opened and may lead to microorganisms being carried into the air on microscopic liquid droplets. In the event of a spill or breakage of a liquid culture, the resulting aerosol cloud is particularly hazardous to those with the task of cleaning it up [see 13.4].

Under the *COSHH Regulations* [see 2.2], an assessment must be made of the risks to health involved in the activities contemplated, particularly bearing in mind the skills and behaviour of pupils [see Ch. 3]. Typically, reference must be made to the general risk assessments listed here in the margin to identify the restrictions and precautions that are to be

Topics Ch.5a, Micro, Handbook Ch. 15.2

---

[1] Administrative Memorandum 3/90 *Animals and Plants in Schools: Legal Aspects* (DES/WO/SOED 1990) provides a useful summary though it is not entirely accurate in relation to capturing animals and collecting plants from the wild (see for example the *CLEAPSS Laboratory Handbook* for correct information).

observed[2]. Work with microorganisms has been defined at three levels of operation (from relatively safe [level 1] to more advanced, requiring appropriate facilities and training [level 3]) and this is exemplified in the references quoted here. (Note that this categorisation should not be confused with that used by professional microbiologists to classify levels of hazard with pathogenic microorganisms.)

DfEE Safety
Ch. 17.4

Culturing samples of microorganisms from the environment (eg, from the soil, the air, raw milk and especially the fingers) may greatly increase the numbers of any pathogens which could be present but *is* permissible if precautions are taken, as discussed below, to ensure that microbes cannot escape from the incubated cultures. Culturing from, for example, toilets, changing rooms, drains, intestinal contents or spots and pimples is particularly hazardous and should **not** be attempted. To avoid encouraging bacteria which can thrive in the human body, all cultures of microorganisms should be incubated at ambient temperatures. If growth must be accelerated, temperatures above 30 °C should not normally be used.

All cultures obtained by sampling the environment should be effectively closed with clear adhesive tape when they are to be examined by pupils. Note, however, that such cultures must **not** be *completely sealed* **before** incubation as this may encourage the growth of extremely dangerous anaerobic pathogens. Instead, for agar plates, the lid should be attached to the base with two or four small strips of adhesive tape. Cultures on agar are always preferable to the use of broth cultures (but avoid blood agar) as they do not present the same level of hazard. If broth cultures **are** used, they should always be contained in toughened glass tubes or bottles, preferably with screw caps and seals (eg, McCartney or Universal bottles) to guard against breakages and spills.

Handbook
Ch. 15.2.11

If pupils are likely to tamper with, and open, cultures, the microorganisms in them must first be killed using 40% aqueous methanal (formalin), taking suitable precautions [see 13.8].

If specific microorganisms are to be cultured, only those thought to present minimum risk, given good practice, should be grown. [Lists of these are given in all the general risk assessments for microbiology, referred to earlier in this section.] All cultures should nevertheless be treated as potentially dangerous because of the possibility of contamination, mutation and incomplete knowledge of the microorganisms' pathogenicity.

Cultures of sporulating microorganisms, especially fungi, need careful handling to avoid the dispersal of spores. The spattering of liquid cultures from inoculation loops when they are flamed should be avoided; this is best achieved by slowly heating the loop from the base towards the tip of the loop.

[2] In Scotland, alternative general risk assessments are used: *Safety in Microbiology: a code of practice for schools and non-advanced further educcation* (Strathclyde Regional Council 1989) plus a supplement *Post 16 Student Work at Level 3* (Strathclyde Regional Council 1991).

13.3 Biotechnology

Topics Ch.5b

Micro

SSERC 180

Handbook
Ch. 14.9,
14.10, 15.2,
15.14

Reprints
Sec. E

Work with fermenters is similar to general microbiology except that it is on a larger scale with consequently higher risks of spills and inevitable aerosol formation. Microorganisms that are cultured must present minimum risk given good practice but all the precautions necessary for smaller-scale microbiology work are just as relevant for studies with fermenters.[3]

Biotechnology investigations involving enzymes pose risks of allergic reactions [see 13.5]. Work involving DNA technology can be accomplished safely if simple precautions are taken. The use of DNA is in itself usually safe but hazards can arise from chemicals (especially acrylamide gels and ethidium bromide [see 13.8]) and electrical equipment employed in the manipulation of DNA. These, however, present well-known risks that are easily dealt with. For example, electrophoresis of DNA fragments should utilise low voltages or equipment which prevents access to connections at high voltages. Tissue culture involves the use of certain chemicals which are harmful and should be handled with care. It should always involve aseptic techniques. Most tissue culture in schools will involve plant materials; if animal cells are cultured it is essential that these are taken from sources which cannot be harbouring human pathogens.

13.4 Dealing with Spills of Microbiological Cultures

Handbook
Ch. 15.2.14

The DfEE recommends that accidental spills should be reported to, and dealt with by, the teacher[4], who should record all incidents, and the room itself should be cleared if a gross spill occurs. It is important to use an appropriate disinfectant, at a suitable concentration and to leave it for a sufficient length of time to be effective.

A prepared microbiology spills kit should be available. If a spill occurs, wearing gloves, cover it with a paper towel or towels and soak with an appropriately-diluted clear phenolic disinfectant solution or Virkon disinfectant solution. A freshly-made 1% aqueous solution of sodium chlorate(I) (hypochlorite) solution may be used but it is quickly rendered inactive by organic matter. A 10% solution is therefore preferable to help guard against this (but care must be taken as this is corrosive).

It should be possible to cover the spill without bringing the face into the aerosol cloud formed above it. The paper towel should be left in place for 15 minutes and then swept into a suitable container and the whole contaminated area disinfected as appropriate. If a spill involves broken glass it may be more appropriate to use a disinfectant in the form of a powder to

---

[3] In Scotland, alternative general risk assessments are used: *Safety in Microbiology: a code of practice for schools and non-advanced further education* (Strathclyde Regional Council 1989) plus a supplement *Post 16 Student Work at Level 3* (Strathclyde Regional Council 1991).

[4] In Scotland, the person trained for work at level 3.

cover the debris before sweeping this into the container. Ideally, the container should then be autoclaved.

Spills on clothing can be treated with Virkon disinfectant or a clear phenolic disinfectant but the latter may stain or leave odours. An alternative, though less effective, disinfectant is an ampholytic surface active type (eg, Griffin and George *ASAB*, Philip Harris *BAS Cleaner*, *Tego MHG*) at the recommended dilution. If skin is contaminated, the affected area can be carefully washed with soap and hot water. If a disinfectant must be used, Virkon or 70% ethanol solution can be employed.

DfEE Safety Ch. 17.4

13.5 Diseases Transmissible Between Animals and Humans (Zoonoses)

Micro

No material likely to introduce pathogens or parasites should be deliberately brought into schools unless adequate procedures are taken to remove the risk of infection to people or resident animals. No dead vertebrates or material taken from them should be brought into schools unless it has been obtained from an abattoir or shop selling it for food (and thus subject to checks by the local authority), or it has been specially prepared for dissection or display. If pupils bring into schools injured or dying birds etc, it is unwise (and often fruitless) to attempt to care for the animals. They should be kept isolated from resident animals, handled with care and humanely killed, as appropriate. Arrangements may need to be made for the transfer of the animals to a local vet or PDSA/RSPCA/ SSPCA centre.

Animals kept in school should be obtained from reputable sources. Correct management is needed to maintain animals in good health and free from pathogens[5]. It is inadvisable for animals from schools to be "boarded out" in domestic premises because proper treatment and handling cannot be ensured, the risk of infection may be greater and escapes may cause problems. Where animals must leave the school premises at holiday times, it is essential that steps are taken to guard against all of the problems outlined above. In addition, small mammals in a colony should **not** be separated when boarded out as there may be problems when the animals are reunited. Written guidance on the care of the animals should be provided for recipients.

Animals can be infected by pathogens from wild animals and also from humans. Dogs and cats, for example, can be infected by the mumps virus and diphtheria bacterium. Wild rats and mice can infect small mammals kept in school with the bacterium *Leptospira*, which can cause the serious Weil's disease in humans either as a result of direct contact with infected animals, or through contact with material contaminated with their urine and excrement. Small mammals in schools must, therefore, be kept in places safe from intrusion by wild rats and mice and all animal bedding and food should be kept in containers safe from contamination.

---

[5] Information on animal maintenance can be obtained from organisations such as CLEAPSS, SSERC, the RSPCA and SSPCA.

When visits to farms are arranged and animals are handled, it should be ensured that good hygiene is practised, and that there is suitable provision for washing and drying hands afterwards. During lambing time, there is a low risk of diseases being transmitted to pregnant women which might lead to abortion. Warnings should be given to females accompanying classes.

Living material which is parasitic in vertebrates, particularly humans, should not be brought into schools. Some nematode eggs are very resistant and can remain viable even after storage for some time in 4% aqueous methanal (10% formalin).

There is rising concern over the risks of dog parasites transferring to children. There is an increasing chance of contact with the eggs of the nematode *Toxacara* which are known to survive for long periods in the soil.

When eyes of cattle are dissected, there is some concern of the possibility of the transmission of the agent causing bovine spongiform encephalopathy (BSE). The risk is, however, only remote and theoretical. It will become increasingly difficult to obtain the eyes of cattle but even if they are available it is prudent to switch to the eyes of pigs (or possibly sheep). The DfEE has advised against the dissection of the eyes of cattle and some employers may have forbidden it.

DfEE Safety
Ch. 17.2

13.6 Allergy

Reprints Sec.E

Handbook
Ch. 14.1.5

A wide range of materials can stimulate an allergic reaction and can cause sensitisation. It should be remembered that a long period can elapse between exposure to an allergen and the development of sensitisation. [See also 4.4 and 14.4.]

Dusts from the skin, hair and feathers of animals and the sap of some plants may be allergenic. Some people show immediate responses; others become sensitised over a period of time [see 15.2]. Symptoms vary in severity and may appear as dermatitis, asthma [see 14.4] or irritation of the membranes of the eyes and nose. People with known allergies should avoid all contact with the allergens responsible. Allergy to locusts is not uncommon and symptoms should be watched for. It is prudent to avoid the **continuous** culture of locusts throughout the year and to keep them in schools only when needed. When animals are kept, it is important to avoid allowing, as far as possible, the formation of dusts of any kind, by careful handling and cleaning.

Some plants cause allergies when handled. Special note should be taken of *Primula*, *Chrysanthemum* and many members of the lily family. Handling hyacinth and other bulbs can cause dermatitis. Some umbellifers, especially the giant hog weed, can cause photosensitisation with skin reactions developing after exposure to sunlight. The allergy to grass pollen (appearing as 'hay fever') is well known; fungal spores can also be allergenic. Some pupils are allergic to peanuts or other nuts and this must be borne in mind if activities involving the burning of nuts are carried out. Pupils may react to the smoke, if the nuts are eaten or, in rare cases, if the nuts are merely handled. When enzyme solutions are prepared, it is important to avoid allowing powders to spread into the air where they can be inhaled. There have been reports of science staff developing allergies to diastase.

SSERC 178

Venoms (for example, bee, ant and wasp venoms) can be allergenic as well as having their direct effects. Stings invariably occur in the course of bee keeping, in spite of the use of protective clothing, which should be insisted upon. The sting should be removed as soon as possible and medical attention sought. Some people become sensitised to bee venom and show signs of severe shock when stung again. Immediate medical attention is required in such cases and the individuals concerned should never take any further part in bee keeping.

Handbook Ch. 15.5.4

DfEE Safety Ch. 17.2, 17.3

Irritants from certain animal and plant materials can produce rashes (eg, stinging nettles) and some caterpillars have hairs which can penetrate the skin and then break off. The hairs of the brown-tail moth (*Euproctis chrysorrhea*) are particularly potent.

13.7 Poisonous Plants

Many wild and garden plants have poisonous parts [see also 13.6]. Nothing should be eaten unless it is known to be edible and non-poisonous. Poisoning commonly occurs when the poisonous material is mistaken for edible material.

The **castor oil plant** (*Ricinis communis*) has seeds with very poisonous coats but the purgative oil extracted from the endosperm is not thought of as a poison. Between 3 and 12 castor oil seeds, when eaten by children, have proved fatal.

Red kidney beans, although often used in cookery, contain toxins which are only de-activated when the beans are boiled.

Laburnum seeds (*L. anagyroides*) are the most common cause of children poisoning themselves with plant material. Children associate them with edible peas because they come from pods.

The **potato plant** (*Solanum tuberosum*) has leaves and fruit which are poisonous but children may expect these to be harmless because the tubers are a common food.

Rhubarb (*Rheum rhaponticum*) has green leaf blades which are poisonous but are not expected to be so because the leaf stalks are eaten as a "fruit".

The **deathcap toadstool** (*Amanita phalloides*), responsible for the great majority of mushroom poisoning fatalities, is thought by victims to look and smell like an edible mushroom.

Poisonous berries are frequently eaten by birds but this does not mean that the berries are safe for people to eat.

Seeds for germination sold commercially (eg, those of many cereals and vegetables) are often dressed with pesticides, many of which are poisonous. All such seeds must be handled with extreme care. Seeds bought from health food shops, however, should be safe.

13.8 Chemicals Used in Biology

Topics

Reprints Sec.C

Hazcards

Handbook
Ch. 20.3

Haz Man

DfEE Safety
Ch. 15.2

Chemicals are often used in biology, not to investigate their properties, but because they have particular uses in tests and investigations. Many biological reagents are often named after their "inventors". Both these aspects may lead to a failure of science staff to appreciate the true hazards of the chemicals in use.

Examples of some of the hazardous substances used in biology are highlighted below [see Ch.15 for a more extensive list of chemicals]. Reference should be made to appropriate risk assessments for a fuller discussion and details of safer substitutes.

Adrenalin is toxic although students will normally use dilute solutions.

Chlorinated hydrocarbons (trichloromethane [chloroform]; tetrachloromethane [carbon tetrachloride]) are toxic and suspected carcinogens [see 15.4].

Colchicine is highly toxic and is not recommended for use in schools.

Enzymes, including those in biological washing powders, may cause allergic reactions; [see also 13.6].

SSERC 180

Ethidium bromide, used as a DNA stain, is a mutagen, and should not be used. DNA kits produced for the UK schools market do not require its use.

Fehling's solution contains corrosive sodium hydroxide which can spit out of a test tube during heating; Benedict's solution, which is safer, should be used instead. The solution should preferably be heated in a water bath.

Flammable liquids such as ethanol and ethoxyethane (diethyl ether) are used in certain procedures. Some stains may be made up in flammable liquids. The use of benzene is now illegal in all educational establishments.

Indoleacetic acid (IAA) is toxic in its pure state but solutions prepared from the solid are so dilute that risks with these are negligible.

Methanal solution (formalin) which is toxic should be used only where necessary − for fixing tissues and killing microorganisms. There are safer alternatives for preserving tissues (eg, Philip Harris *Opresol*, propylene phenoxetol).

SSERC 79

Millon's reagent tests for tyrosine in proteins and contains a toxic mercury salt in concentrated nitric acid. Its use should be restricted to the sixth form under supervision. Cole's modification[6] of the reagent, which is safer, should, however, always be used, if the Millon's test is contemplated. The Biuret test is safer still, but nevertheless contains sodium hydroxide

---

[6]   For details, refer to *Hazcards* 'Mercury compounds', *Handbook* Ch 7.10.10. or *Haz Man*.

which is corrosive. *Albustix* may be used safely but these do not test for all proteins. The Sakaguchi test will detect the presence of arginine but this is more complicated than other tests for proteins.

Ninhydrin is classified as harmful (but in formulations sold in spray cans it is diluted and these are classified as highly flammable because of the spray propellant). It is *not* classified as a proven carcinogen, despite a widespread belief to the contrary. It should nevertheless be used with care in a fume cupboard.

Phenylthiocarbamide [PTC] (phenylthiourea [PTU]), is **not** harmful when used in taste-testing investigations, if only impregnated swabs or paper strips are used [see 14.4].

SSERC 60

Hazcards

Pyrogallate solution (alkaline benzene-1,2,3-triol) is used in tests for, or measurements of, oxygen in gas samples because of its oxygen-absorbing properties. It is often made up in a very concentrated (often saturated) solution of sodium or potassium hydroxide which is very hazardous to prepare and use. It can be made up in aqueous solution and mixed with alkali at the time of use. It is not, however, always necessary to use such a highly alkaline solution; pyrogallol can be made up in a saturated sodium hydrogencarbonate solution which is safer.

Stains and indicators are often impure and their harmful effects may not have been well researched. Materials which react with substances in living tissue should always be somewhat suspect. Care should be taken when handling the solids; solutions should possibly be made up in a fume cupboard. The solutions used by pupils will be dilute and usually of minimal hazard.

13.9 Disposal of Biological Material

Topics Ch.5a

Handbook Ch. 15.12

For the disposal of all cultures of microorganisms, autoclaving is always recommended in preference to the use of chemical disinfection. The use of a purpose-built incinerator is an effective alternative and can be used to dispose of autoclaved materials. (Note that sodium chlorate(I) (hypochlorite) solution is inactivated by organic matter. If chemical disinfection **has** to be used, a suitable solution of a clear phenolic disinfectant or Virkon disinfectant should be employed.) Contaminated equipment should be autoclaved before reuse or disposal.

Handbook Ch. 14.1.7, 14.6

If animals are to be killed, this must be done humanely. Dead bodies, other remains and contaminated material (such as soiled bedding from animal cages) should be disposed of in such a way that they do not become a health hazard. Typically, this will involve sealing in opaque plastic bags before disposal with normal refuse or, preferably, by incineration.

14 Using Pupils as the Subjects of Investigation

14.1 Body Measurements

The educational advantage of any procedure should be weighed against the hazards involved. Procedures should never exceed those routinely undertaken in supervised games or athletics. There must be no pressure on pupils to take part in any investigation on themselves.

Any pupil who is medically excused normal school PE activities should not take part in investigations on breathing and pulse rate, the operation of temperature-regulating activities of the body, etc. Teachers should be tactful in the arrangements made for excluding pupils from such activities, so that undue attention is not focused on non-participants.

DfEE Safety Ch. 17.5

The purpose of investigations on pupils may be, in part, to illustrate natural variation. Excessive and potentially damaging competition between pupils is educationally undesirable, may be hazardous and should be avoided. Pupils should be reminded that any measurements taken are approximate and must not be taken as medically relevant.

Handbook Ch. 11.8

When taking samples of breath, teachers should be aware of possible dizziness or fainting resulting from forced breathing, such as hyperventilation, breathing too quickly or slowly, or holding of breath. Teachers should know of the emergency aid measures required in the event of pupils getting into difficulty including the liability to injury as a result of fainting or falls. Training is required in the safe use of the spirometer and similar pieces of equipment.

Handbook Ch. 14.5

Mouthpieces, for example of spirometers and clinical thermometers used for taking body temperature measurements should be disinfected before and after use in ethanol or a fresh solution of "Milton" disinfectant at the appropriate dilution, allowing adequate time for disinfection to occur (ethanol: 2-5 minutes; Milton: 15-30 minutes). They should be rinsed in water before use.

All equipment used for exercise, such as exercise bicycles or step-up benches should be checked for security, stability and adequate surrounding clearance before use.

14.2 Human Cell Sampling

Because of a small risk of transmission of the AIDS-causing virus (HIV), the DfEE recommends that blood samples should not be taken from staff or pupils. Most education employers follow this advice and do not permit blood sampling. However it is permitted by some employers in a few specific instances, eg some post-16 vocational courses. Teachers **must** follow their employer's local rules.

SSERC 178

Samples of time-expired blood from a blood bank may be used. Autoclaving of such blood and contaminated equipment is recommended before disposal.

> If blood sampling **is** carried out, sterile procedures must be strictly enforced and all material contaminated with blood autoclaved before disposal or treatment.

Many education employers now allow human cheek cell sampling provided safe procedures are strictly followed. Teachers should consider the extent to which pupils can be relied on to follow these procedures before undertaking practicals involving cheek cell sampling.

Handbook
Ch. 14.4

> A safe procedure for cheek cell sampling has been proposed by the Institute of Biology. Using cotton buds from a newly-opened pack, swab the inside of the mouth around the gums. The sample can be smeared onto a clean slide and covered with a cover slip and stained if required. Used cotton buds, slides and coverslips should be placed immediately after use into freshly-made 1% sodium chlorate(I) (hypochlorite) solution.

Reprints Sec.E

SSERC 178

14.3 Using Human Body Fluids

Topics Ch.4

Contrary to what many teachers believe, the use of saliva for investigations is, and always has been, allowed in schools. However, there is always some risk of spreading saliva-borne infections such as tuberculosis (TB). Pupils (and technicians) should only handle their own saliva, including its disposal and rinsing equipment after use. All contaminated equipment should be autoclaved or disinfected in a freshly-prepared 1% aqueous solution of sodium chlorate(I) (hypochlorite) before cleaning. This, coupled with usual safe hygienic practices (washing hands etc), will ensure that any risks become negligible [see Ch 4].

Handbook
Ch. 14.4

SSERC 178

Investigations using urine only become hazardous if pupils (or staff) come into contact with urine other than their own. Pupils should wash their own glassware and technicians should wear gloves when subsequently handling it. Disinfection using a freshly-made 1% aqueous solution of sodium chlorate(I) (hypochlorite) or autoclaving is recommended.

When contemplating an investigation on the effect on excretion of increasing students' dietary intake of salt, teachers should take steps to ensure that the moderate amount of salt added to food will not be "contra-indicated" by checking with the students.

14.4 Tasting and Smelling Activities, and Using Cosmetics

Topics Ch.4

Handbook
Ch. 15.13

Investigations involving tasting and the associated sense of smell should use only foodstuffs and chemicals known to be harmless [see Ch. 4]. To avoid any risk of contamination, such substances should be kept apart from other chemicals used by pupils. Avoid foods known to have irritant or allergenic effects such as chilli peppers, peanuts or other nuts. Strict hygienic practices must be enforced and if possible such investigations should be done in rooms other than the laboratory (eg food rooms).

For advice on smelling substances other than those also being tasted, see Chapter 4.

Teachers should be aware of the possible hazards when tasting PTC (phenylthiocarbamide; also known as PTU, phenylthiourea). Use only paper strips containing no more than 0.1 mg of PTC. The stock solution and solid compound should be locked away and must never be used in tasting investigations.

Pupils who have made cosmetics will often, naturally, wish to try them out. If this is the case then departments should keep separate stocks of chemicals which are only used for this purpose and all benches and equipment used must be scrupulously clean. If possible make the cosmetics in an HE room. Be aware that some pupils may be allergic to some ingredients.

14.5 Electrical Monitoring, Stimulation and Biological Feedback

Equipment used to monitor electrical activity in the body requires low-resistance skin contacts which increase the risk of electric shock. All such equipment must be isolated from mains voltages, eg by the use of optical fibre connections [see 11.6].

Teachers may not use electrical stimulation to produce muscle contractions in pupils unless the activity, including the equipment used, has been specifically sanctioned by the Community Health Physician.

Unpleasant physiological effects can be produced by rhythmical impulses, either light or sound. The frequency of 7 Hz is often singled out as hazardous but other frequencies are also dangerous [see 12.1].

15 Hazardous Chemicals

15.1 Introduction

Reprints
Sec. C,
Hazcards,
Topics,
Haz Man
DfEE Safety
Ch. 15.2

A mythology has grown up over the years concerning "banned" chemicals. In fact very few chemicals are banned nationally from use in schools. Some employers have issued their own restrictions. This chapter deals with the problems that may be encountered in schools etc while using chemicals. It is not intended to be an exhaustive guide to all chemicals that may be met with but a discussion of the more common problems. Various publications give much more detail.

15.2 Types of Hazard

Chemicals may be hazardous for one or more of the following reasons. They may be corrosive or irritant. They may be toxic or harmful by ingestion, skin absorption or inhalation. However there is no simple definition of toxicity or unambiguous method of measuring it. Some compounds are known to be human carcinogens, while others are suspected. Opinions are continually revised as more research is done. Teachers need to consult publications such as *Education in Science*, published by ASE, the CLEAPSS *Bulletin* or SSERC *Bulletin* to ensure their information is up to date. Risk assessments will then need to be amended accordingly. Highly flammable substances, oxidising agents and reducing agents present their own special hazards. Some substances are hazardous as solids, or in concentrated solutions, but may be suitable for use by pupils in dilute solutions. It is vital that after any contact with chemicals, teachers, technicians and pupils should wash their hands thoroughly, and facilities should be provided for this. The most probable risk to health in terms of toxicity is by the inhalation route.

HAZARD CATEGORISATIONS
The following is a summary of the hazard categorisations as defined by the *CHIP Regulations*. [See 7.9 for relevant safety signs.]

Categories based on physico-chemical properties

Explosive. These are compounds that show a risk or extreme risk of explosion by shock, friction, fire or other source of ignition. Included in this category are **organic peroxides** and **picric acid**.

Oxidising. These are compounds that are defined as having flammable properties even when not in contact with other combustible materials, or may cause fire or explosion on contact with combustible materials or are explosive when mixed with combustible materials (eg **potassium chlorate(V)**).

Extremely flammable. These are materials that have a flash point [see 15.6] lower than 0 °C and a boiling point lower than or equal to 35 °C, (eg **ethoxyethane**).

Highly flammable. This category includes those compounds that are spontaneously flammable in air (eg **aluminium dust**), those that are highly flammable with flash points below 21 °C which are not extremely flammable, those gases or preparations that are flammable in air at normal pressure (eg **hydrogen sulphide**), gaseous substances that are flammable in air at normal pressure when supplied as liquid (eg **lpg**) and those substances that release a highly flammable gas when in contact with water (eg water-reactive **hydrides**).

Flammable. These are liquids with a flash point equal to or greater than 21 °C and less than or equal to 55 °C (eg **paraffin**).

Categorisation on the basis of health effects

Very toxic (eg **hydrogen sulphide**), **toxic** (eg **chlorine**), **harmful** (eg **ammonium chloride**) are classifications based on the effect occurring when the material is swallowed, contacts the skin or is inhaled. The classification is based on the effect of the material on various animals.

Corrosive. These are materials that cause burns. If a material causes burns when in contact with skin for three minutes or less it is classified as causing severe burns. If burning occurs in 4 hours or less it is classified as causing burns (eg **concentrated sulphuric acid**).

Irritant. Materials that cause significant inflammation of the skin when left in contact with the skin for 4 hours and which is present after 24 hours or more are classified as irritant to the skin. Materials that cause ocular lesions within 72 hours and which persist for at least 24 hours are classified as irritant to the eyes (eg **potassium carbonate**).

Sensitising. These are defined as materials causing sensitisation if the material is swallowed, contacts the skin or is inhaled, (eg **cobalt**). (Sensitisation means that further exposure to the material produces an unusually severe reaction even when the dose is less than before or the exposure time is reduced.)

[See 15.4 for information about **carcinogens**, **mutagens** and compounds **toxic for reproduction**.]

Categorisation based on environmental effects

These are substances dangerous for the environment. They include materials that are dangerous in the aquatic environment in that they are very toxic to aquatic organisms, may cause long-term adverse effects or may be harmful to the aquatic environment. They also include materials that are classified as dangerous to the non-aquatic environment including materials toxic to flora, fauna and soil organisms those that may cause long-term adverse effects to the environment and those dangerous for the ozone layer (eg **CFCs**).

15.3 Occupational Exposure Limits

The Health and Safety Executive publishes tables of Occupational Exposure Limits[1], but teachers will not normally have the facilities to test air samples for contaminants at these concentrations. It should be borne in mind that, while pupils will not be exposed for the length of time envisaged when drawing up the limits, young people may be more sensitive than adults and that some chemicals have Short Term Exposure Limits, where exposure for as little as 15 minutes can have adverse health effects. In general teachers and technicians may be more at risk, particularly if they are forced to work in an ill-ventilated preparation room.

Table 15.1

Odour threshold values (ppm by volume)			
ammonia	0.03 – 2.7	hydrogen sulphide	0.01
carbon disulphide	0.08 – 0.65	nitrogen dioxide	1 – 5
chlorine	1 – 5	methanal	0.07
hydrogen chloride	1 – 5	sulphur dioxide	1

Table 15.2[2]

Occupational Exposure Limits (ppm by volume)					
	8 hour	15 min		8 hour	15 min
ammonia	25	35	hydrogen sulphide	10	15
carbon disulphide	10	maximum exp. limit	methanal	2	maximum exp. limit
chlorine	0.5	1	nitrogen dioxide	3	5
hydrogen chloride	–	5	sulphur dioxide	2	5

[1]   Guidance Note EH40 *Occupational Exposure Limits*, published annually by the HSE.
[2]   Taken from *EH40/95 Occupational Exposure Limits 1995*, HSE, 1995

The human nose is a sensitive detection instrument and can give a good indication when potential problems are likely to arise. However, it cannot always be trusted as the sense of smell can become fatigued. The ranges given in Table 15.1 recognise the existence of considerable variation in individual sensitivity. Except for **hydrogen sulphide**, if these chemicals are clearly detected by their smell, their recommended concentration limit may well have been exceeded locally. If eye or lung irritation is induced, the concentrations are almost certain to be much too high. As a way of introducing safety topics[3], more able, older pupils might be encouraged to use data for Occupational Exposure Limits to calculate "safe" masses of chemicals that might be used in practical work where a hazard exists. Investigations have shown that the level of nitrogen dioxide produced when a class of 24 pupils carried out the thermal decomposition of a metal nitrate on a test tube scale and the amounts of sulphur dioxide generated by the reaction of an acid with a sulphite did not exceed the Occupational Exposure Limits[4].

15.4 Carcinogenic Chemicals

The number of chemicals that are thought to possess carcinogenic properties has increased over recent years and some of these are likely to be found in schools. There is a danger that the emotive subject of cancer will cause relatively remote risks to be exaggerated compared with the more immediate hazards from fire etc. Of the many substances met with in industry which are known or suspected carcinogens, comparatively few are likely to be met with in schools. Many carcinogenic chemicals also have other, more rapid, toxic effects and their carcinogenic action may ultimately result from such effects. If handled while observing the precautions that their more immediate toxic effects warrant, their carcinogenic effects should present little danger. Examples of such compounds are given in the next section. However, it may be that some carcinogenic chemicals are treated with insufficient care because they have a relatively small short term toxic effect – tobacco smoke being an example.

A small number of chemicals encountered in schools are thought to be toxic for reproduction (teratogenic), ie they may cause birth defects; these are also discussed in the next section.

The Health and Safety Commission in its publication[5] defines categories of carcinogens, mutagens and materials toxic for reproduction. A Scottish Office circular[6] gives more detail.

---

[3] *Preparing COSHH Risk Assessments for Project Work in Schools*, SSERC, 1991
[4] See *Educ. Chem.*, 1986, **23**, 79
[5] *Chemicals (Hazard Information and Packaging) Regulations 1994* [the *CHIP2 Regulations*]: *Approved Guide to the Classification and Labelling of Substances and Preparations Dangerous for Supply*
[6] *Guidance on the Use of Carcinogenic Substances in Work in Schools and in Non-advanced Work in Further Education Colleges*, Circular 78/95, SOED, 1995

Carcinogenic substances

Category 1 Substances known to be carcinogenic in humans. (These are either totally banned in schools or their use is severely restricted.) Examples which might be met with in schools include **nickel(II) oxide** and **zinc chromate(VI)** solids.

Category 2 Substances which should be regarded as if they are carcinogenic in humans. (These should be avoided if possible in schools and if their use is necessary they are to be used only after the appropriate risk assessment which must involve the very tightest control of their use.) Examples which might be met with in schools include **1,2-dibromoethane**, **carbon disulphide** and **salts of hydrazine**.

Category 3 Substances which cause concern for humans owing to possible carcinogenic effects but in respect of which there is insufficient data to make a satisfactory assessment or place them in category 2, or tumours are only produced in test animals fed on very high dose levels. The use of these needs to be monitored. While such substances should be handled with care, schools should not feel inhibited in using them where there is a good educational reason to do so. Examples which might be met with in schools include **nickel sulphate** and **carbonate**, **phenylamine** and **methanal**.

Mutagenic substances

Category 1 Substances known to be mutagenic in humans. These are defined as those for which sufficient evidence has been established to show a causal association between human exposure to a substance and heritable genetic damage.

Category 2 Substances which should be regarded as if they are mutagenic in humans. For these there is sufficient extra evidence to provide a strong presumption of a causal association between human exposure to a substance and heritable genetic damage.

Category 3 Substances which cause concern for humans because of possible mutagenic effects. For these there is some evidence but not enough to place the substance in category 2.

Toxic for reproduction

Category 1 Substances known to be toxic for reproduction in humans (ie can cross the placenta wall and cause birth deformity or mutation).

Category 2 Substances which should be regarded as toxic for reproduction in humans.

The following are examples of **carcinogenic chemicals** which may be found in schools.

Ammonium dichromate(VI) should be heated in a fume cupboard because of the risk of the decomposition products containing category 1 carcinogens.

Asbestos. (Category 1 carcinogen). All forms of asbestos are now banned from use in schools. Suitable alternatives are available.

- Ceramic tiles and oil-tempered hardboard sheets can replace asbestos mats.
- Asbestos wool can be replaced by ceramic wool (including platinised ceramic wool) or "Rocksil" (which should be roasted before use as it may contain oxidisable impurities). These are also fibrous and should be used with care.
- Vermiculite can be used in the "wet asbestos" technique (time needs to be allowed for the liquid to soak into the solid).

Topics Ch.9

Aromatic amines and their salts (Category 1 carcinogens). The following compounds or their salts must not be kept or prepared in school laboratories: **naphthalen-1-amine (1-naphthylamine)**, **naphthalen-2-amine (2-naphthylamine)**, **biphenyl-4,4'-diamine (benzidine)**, and other **amino-substituted biphenyls** (see reference for full list).

Azo dyes should be chosen with care. The water-soluble ones are less likely to be carcinogenic (eg methyl orange). The solid dye should not be isolated.

Benzene (Category 1 carcinogen). The use of benzene for all educational purposes is now illegal[7]. The effect of this is to preclude the use of commercial petrol for experimental purposes as it contains $> 0.1\%$ benzene.

Benzidine (biphenyl-4,4'-diamine) (Category 1 carcinogen). It is possible that this substance might be encountered in schools as it was used as a test for blood and lignin.

Carbon disulphide (Category 2 carcinogen) is not recommended for use in schools. As well as being highly flammable and very toxic, it is toxic for reproduction and may cause birth defects. Methylbenzene is safer as a solvent in the preparation of sulphur allotropes. Ethyl 3-phenylpropenoate (cinnamate) can be used in place of carbon disulphide in a hollow prism to produce a white light spectrum.

Chloroethene (vinyl chloride) (Category 1 carcinogen). This monomer could be produced when investigating the effect of heat on plastics. Such investigations should be carried out on a very small scale in a fume cupboard.

Chromium(VI) compounds. As well as being toxic by inhalation and causing skin sensitisation, **insoluble chromates** are classified as Category I carcinogens. Insoluble chromates produced by precipitation reactions should never be dried out as the dust is the major hazard. Precipitates should be washed away with a large volume of water. Potassium and sodium chromate(VI) are classified as irritant.

---

[7]   *COSHH (Amendment) Regulations 1991*

1,2-dibromoethane (ethylene dibromide) (Category 2 carcinogen). This compound should not be kept in schools. It may be produced in the reaction between bromine water and ethene on a test tube scale but does not present a hazard as very little if any of the carcinogen is formed. The product should not be isolated.

Hydrazine and its salts (Category 2 carcinogens) are toxic and not recommended for schools.

Lead ethanoate (lead acetate) (Category 3 carcinogen and toxic for reproduction category 1). Its use in schools should be avoided. Lead nitrate is a safer alternative for reactions of lead in solution or for testing for hydrogen sulphide but should be treated as though it is toxic for reproduction.

Methanal (formaldehyde) (Category 3 carcinogen). This can react with hydrogen chloride to produce the potent carcinogen *bis*-chloromethyl ether. There is, however, no evidence that such a reaction can occur in schools and the product is not produced by mixing the vapours. However, cleaning of glassware that may have contained methanal needs care if there is a chance of the washings mixing with the acid in drains. In the preparation of methanal polymers with phenol, the hydrochloric acid catalyst can be replaced by 50% sulphuric acid.

Nickel(II) compounds. Dusts of these compounds are suspected carcinogens and may cause skin sensitisation. The use of crystalline salts and compounds in schools for solution reactions and crystallization etc should not present a problem but care should be taken to prevent dusts of the oxide or anhydrous salts being produced. The use of **nickel(II) oxide** (Category 1 carcinogen) is not recommended in schools. Several common salts are classified as Category 3 carcinogens, eg **nickel sulphate** and **carbonate**.

Phenylamine (aniline) is highly toxic and a Category 3 carcinogen. Chlorobenzene can be used to replace phenylamine in some physics experiments as it has similar properties.

Potassium bromate (Category 2 carcinogen). This compound is toxic if swallowed but should not present problems if used in reactions of bromates in solution.

Tetracarbonylnickel(0) (nickel carbonyl) must not be prepared as it is highly toxic. It is a Category 3 carcinogen and toxic for reproduction Category 2.

Tetrachloromethane (carbon tetrachloride) (Category 3 carcinogen) should not be used as a solvent. It should be used only where there is no alternative (eg where unique properties are shown). Hexane or cyclohexane should be used for testing for bromine or iodine, care being taken with the flammability of the liquid. Cyclohexane is also a suitable alternative solvent for the acid chloride used in the production of nylon in the laboratory.

Trichloromethane (**chloroform**) (Category 3 carcinogen). See tetrachloromethane, above.

15.5 Other Toxic Chemicals

All toxic chemicals should be kept in a securely locked cupboard or store [see Ch. 16].

Arsenic compounds are extremely toxic. Their use in schools is not recommended.

Barium compounds, other than barium sulphate, are generally classified as "harmful" but should be treated with care.

Bromine should only be used in a fume cupboard. It is also very corrosive and a solution of sodium thiosulphate (concentration 1 M or 20%) should always be at hand when bromine is used. A preliminary rinse with this before washing any contaminated skin lessens the risk of burns. The low viscosity, high density and high volatility of the bromine cause problems when using a teat pipette.

Chlorine should always be prepared and used in a fume cupboard. Some people show hyper-reactivity, and can be affected by relatively trivial concentrations, commonly one hundred to one thousand times lower than for the majority. Such problems are more common than is generally recognised. Explosions have occurred where concentrated sulphuric acid has been used inadvertently in place of hydrochloric acid in the preparation of chlorine via the reaction with potassium manganate(VII). For this reason the preparation of the gas needs great care and alternative methods of preparation such as the action of acid on chlorate(I) (hypochlorite) should be considered [see 4.4]. Cylinders of chlorine should not be used in schools.

Cyanides are extremely toxic and are not recommended for use in schools.

Fluorine should not be prepared or used in schools.

Hydrogen sulphide is as toxic as hydrogen cyanide. In moderate concentrations it anaesthetises the sense of smell and thus the danger may not be realised.

Iodine vapour is harmful and can affect the eyes in particular. All heating reactions (unless in tiny quantities with a loose mineral wool plug in the end of the tube) should be carried out in a fume cupboard.

Haz Man

Mercury. Every precaution must be taken against spills by working over a tray. A build up of mercury vapour may be avoided by using only in a well-ventilated room. The major risk is the long-term exposure to small quantities of mercury vapour. Therefore the metal should never be left open to the air for very long and spills should be dealt with at once [see 7.7].

Mercury compounds (including **Millon's reagent**) which are soluble in water are highly toxic. The use of Cole's modification makes it much less hazardous [see 13.8].

Naphthalene is toxic by skin absorption and by inhalation of the vapour. It may be heated in small quantities outside a fume cupboard providing there is a loose mineral wool plug at the end of the tube. It should not be used for cooling curves where the following are suitable: octadecanoic acid (mp 71.5 °C), hexadecan-1-ol (mp 50 °C), phenyl 2-hydroxybenzoate (salol) (mp 43 °C) or cyclohexane (mp 6.5 °C).

Nitrogen dioxide. This gas is very toxic [see 15.3 for note on heating nitrates].

Procion Yellow and other **dye stuffs**. Some of these are sensitisers, eg the Procion dyes. The dust may cause problems. The solutions should be prepared by staff working at a fume cupboard. The solutions do not present a hazard.

*Reprints
Sec. C & E*

Topics Ch. 8

Osmium(VIII) oxide (**osmic acid**). This material is not recommended for use in schools. Sudan dyes are an alternative for the identification of fats microscopically. However some suppliers list these dyes as suspected carcinogens.

Phenols are very toxic by skin absorption, and can cause serious burns. Areas of skin contact should be washed with soap and water and then glycerol (propan-1,2,3-triol) applied or, better, polyethylene glycol rubbed into the skin to help prevent blisters.

Phosphine is extremely toxic; a fume cupboard should always be used and only small quantities prepared.

Plastics. Investigations involving the heating or burning of plastics require great care and should be done in a fume cupboard, since the products of the breakdown may be toxic, as in the case of pvc, or lachrymatory in the case of "Perspex". Acrylates are also sensitisers.

Sodium nitrite is toxic.

Vanadium compounds are harmful.

15.6 Flammable Liquids

Flammability is classified according to flash point and auto-ignition point [see Table 15.3].

Flash point. This is the lowest temperature at which a liquid gives off vapour at the surface in sufficient quantity to ignite with air when a spark or flame is applied.

Table 15.3 *Flash and Auto-Ignition Points*

Substance	Flash point/°C	Auto-ignition point/°C
motor spirit (ie petrol)	< −40	350 − 450
petroleum spirit 40-60 (petroleum		
ether)	−40	240
ethoxyethane (diethyl ether)	−40	180
carbon disulphide	−30	100
ethanal (acetaldehyde)	−27	185
cyclohexane	−20	260
propanone (acetone)	−17	538
methylbenzene (toluene)	4.5	550
methanol (methyl alcohol)	10	430
ethanol (ethyl alcohol) (95% alcohol,		
74 op)	12	400
pyridine	20	550
butan-2-ol	24	406
1,3- and 1,4-dimethylbenzene (*m*-,		
and *p*-xylene)	25	480
pentyl ethanoate (amyl acetate)	25	380
butan-1-ol	29	365
pentan-1-ol	33	300
white spirit (paint solvent)	39	260
ethanoic anhydride (acetic		
anhydride)	40	380
pentan-2-ol	41	343-385
ethanoic acid (glacial acetic acid)	43	425
paraffin, domestic	47	227
bromobenzene	51	566
benzaldehyde	64	191
cyclohexanol	68	300

Auto-ignition point. This is the temperature at or above which vapour from a liquid will inflame spontaneously in the presence of air. This may be relevant if solvent is dropped on to an electric hot plate.

Flammable liquids commonly met in school science

Ethanal. This substance is extremely flammable and small quantities of acid or alkali can cause it to polymerise violently. If required for use with older pupils it is best kept in small quantities in appropriately labelled bottles.

Ethanol is highly flammable and has caused many accidents in schools when used as a solvent, as a fuel, or in reactions involving its oxidation to ethanoic acid or ethanal [see 4.4, 5.3, and 6.2].

Ethoxyethane (diethyl ether) is extremely flammable. Great care must be taken in its use as the dense vapour can spread over long distances and is easily ignited by sparks from electrical switches as well as naked flames.

Only senior pupils under strict supervision should be allowed to use this substance. It is recommended that the compound is not prepared in schools other than under the strictest supervision with higher level students and in the very smallest of quantities. Any prepared material should not be stored. Ethers from which peroxides have been removed should be used at once and not stored as the inhibitors are also removed and the usual potassium iodide test, for the presence of peroxides, is unreliable.

Pyridine. This substance is highly flammable and all naked flames should be extinguished if it is in use.

15.7 Other Hazardous Chemicals

Aluminium powder should not be freely accessible to pupils.

Ammoniacal silver nitrate (Tollen's Reagent) becomes explosive on standing due to the formation of silver azide. The reagent should not be stored, but prepared freshly in the smallest quantity needed when required. Any unused reagent should be washed away immediately and the test tube cleaned at once.

Aqua Regia is not stable and if needed should be made using a fume cupboard and used at once. It should not be stored.

Di(benzenecarbonyl) peroxide (benzoyl peroxide) has caused explosions. Its role as a catalyst in several organic polymerisations can be safely taken over by di(dodecanoyl) peroxide (lauroyl peroxide).

Chlorates(V) are not suitable for the preparation of oxygen using the so-called **"oxygen mixture"** (potassium chlorate(V) and manganese(IV) oxide). A safer method uses 20 volume hydrogen peroxide with the catalyst, manganese(IV) oxide, just covered with water before the peroxide is added.

Fehling's solution No. 2 contains sodium hydroxide at greater than normal bench reagent concentration and should only be used under the strictest supervision with younger students, all heating being carried out in a water bath. Benedict's solution provides a much safer alternative.

Gaseous hydrocarbons all form explosive mixtures with air.

Reprints
Sec. A & C

Hydrogen/air mixtures are the commonest cause of accidental explosions in school laboratories, particularly in reactions in which metal oxides are being reduced [see Ch. 4].

SSERC 146

Hydrogen/oxygen mixtures. Large-scale ignition of these mixtures can cause a hazard and the reaction is not recommended for experimental work in schools [see Ch. 4]. However, the small-scale production of the mixture of hydrogen and oxygen during electrolysis may be tested provided suitable precautions are taken. [See also 9.4].

Hydrogen peroxide, 100 volume, (30% w/w) should not be handled by pupils. This solution reacts violently with finely divided metals. Hydrogen peroxide should be safe to store in a cool place, provided that it is kept free from impurities which could catalyse its decomposition.

Reprints Sec. C

Ion exchange resins expand very considerably when soaked in water. If confined in a narrow tube such as a burette, the latter may shatter. The resin should always be allowed to soak in a wide container such as a beaker, before transfer to the burette.

Lithium has been known to explode violently when heated on porcelain fragments. This hazard can be avoided if lithium is heated on a combustion spoon.

Magnesium powder should not be freely accessible to pupils. **Magnesium ribbon** provides a temptation for pupils and it should never be left unattended.

Peroxides. Solid peroxides are both oxidising and corrosive.

Phosphorus must be used only in very small quantities with due understanding of its properties. Phosphorus, carelessly discarded into waste boxes or plastic sinks, has given rise to serious delayed-action fires. White phosphorus should only be used by staff, not students, and should be cut while it is immersed in water in a strong vessel such as a mortar. A bottle of copper sulphate solution should be available to deal with any spill of phosphorus [see 17.3]. Bottles containing sodium (or potassium) and white phosphorus should not be on the bench at the same time [see 4.4].

Reprints Sec. C

Potassium and **sodium** must be used only in very small quantities with due understanding of their properties. Bottles containing sodium (or potassium) and white phosphorus should not be on the bench at the same time. Stocks of potassium should be checked on a regular basis (ie once a year) for signs of deterioration: a yellow surface coating indicates the build up of a superoxide layer. Attempts should not be made to cut the yellow layer off the lump of metal. Small samples of potassium can be destroyed by reaction with dry 2-methylpropan-2-ol [see Ch. 16].

Silicon tetrachloride is readily hydrolysed and the product can firmly seal a stopper in place and allow pressure to build up in the container. Bottles containing silicon tetrachloride have been known to burst in store, or on being opened. Any bottle of this, or any other water reactive chloride, should be opened with considerable caution in a fume cupboard, after covering the bottle with a dry cloth. It is particularly dangerous to return unused chemical to the bottle.

Sodium chlorate(I) (hypochlorite) and **domestic bleaches**, as well as being oxidising agents, are very dangerous to skin and eyes, even in dilute solutions. Their very familiarity may induce a false sense of security. Eye protection should be worn.

Sodium and potassium hydroxide solid and **solutions**. The corrosive nature of these common substances, even in the most dilute of solution, means that eye protection should be worn at all times when they are in use. The solids and very concentrated solutions should only be handled by older pupils. For most purposes below the sixth form, solutions less than 0.5 M are perfectly satisfactory and much safer.

Sulphur dioxide canisters frequently cause trouble because the valve seizes up as a result of corrosion. The canisters should not be stored with other corrosive chemicals or in a fume cupboard; an open shelf is generally satisfactory provided the canister cannot roll off! Problems can occur if the valve is screwed down too tightly as this opens up the punctured hole in the canister which is then not closed after further use. (The manufacture of these canisters is being phased out.) [See 16.3.]

Sulphuric acid (concentrated) is very corrosive. When diluting it, always add the acid slowly to water with stirring. Avoid using the acid as a drying agent: there are reports of accidents resulting from blocked apparatus or explosions in which the main damage was caused by the acid used in this way. Silica gel is nearly always an acceptable (and recyclable) alternative. If a liquid must be used, then a saturated aqueous solution of calcium chloride is quite effective.

2,4,6-trinitrophenol (picric acid) is stable if kept wet, but when dry can explode by friction, shock or heat. It forms very sensitive explosive compounds with metals. If the material must be used, it should be in solution and the stocks checked regularly (ie at least once a term) to ensure the contents are not drying out.

Zinc powder should not be freely accessible to pupils.

15.8 Mixtures

Mixtures of oxidising and reducing agents may explode on heating, by friction, or on impact. It is wise to test mixtures beforehand, by heating cautiously a small sample, before allowing pupils to repeat the procedure. Mixtures must be prepared only on the instructions of staff. It is illegal to make gunpowder and other explosives without a licence.

Unexpected accidents have been reported which have resulted from the following mixtures. In most cases, marked * below, heating was necessary. Table 15.4 indicates mixtures which should not be made. Some of these mixtures will "self-heat" if the air is damp. Table 15.5 indicates those that could be made and used, provided suitably strict precautions are adopted. These mixtures should be made up as required and not kept. Some accidents have been caused by unintended mixtures, eg the use of dirty or contaminated apparatus, or by traces of water.

Table 15.4 *Mixtures which should not be made*

* magnesium powder	with	ammonium dichromate(VI)
magnesium powder	with	silver nitrate *(explodes violently on contact with water)*
* magnesium powder	with	sulphur
* aluminium powder	with	lead oxides
* aluminium powder	with	copper(II) oxide
* reducing agents	with	lead(II) nitrate
* tin(II) chloride	with	bismuth(III) nitrate
concentrated sulphuric acid	with	potassium manganate(VII) (permanganate)
trichloromethane (chloroform)	with	propanone (acetone) *(the mixture may react violently due to basic impurities; use ethyl ethanoate in place of the propanone)*
* carbon *or* sulphur	with	potassium nitrate

Table 15.5 *Mixtures which should be handled with strict precautions*

* organic compounds	with	copper(II) oxide
* zinc powder	with	sulphur
* aluminium powder	with	iodine
* aluminium powder	with	iron(III) oxide ("thermite")
* sodium metabisulphite	with	potassium chlorate
potassium chlorate	with	manganese(IV) oxide ("oxygen mixture"). *Not suitable for storage.*

15.9 Dealing with Spills

Whenever chemicals are in use, there is a risk of spills of liquid or solid, the escape of gas or the production of a substance that needs disposal. A well organised department will have available a general spills kit to deal with most chemicals and a special spills kit to deal with mercury [see Ch. 7]. The use of such kits should form part of an in-house training programme for all staff.

Staff should make themselves aware of the potential risks associated with any experiment and ensure that the appropriate neutralising materials are to hand. In the event of a spill resulting in bodily contact or contamination of clothing, **priority should be given to treatment of persons involved** [see 17.1] before tackling the clearing up of the spill.

Solids

Solids may be gathered with a small shovel, or dust pan and brush taking care to avoid raising any dust. The area should then be wiped with a damp disposable cloth unless the spilt material is water reactive and the brush cleaned by washing in a large volume of water. Highly reactive solids such as the alkali metals are best gathered using tongs. Phosphorus can also be dealt with in this way but needs to be dowsed with water during the operation and the affected area treated with copper(II) sulphate solution. With spills of strong oxidising agents special care is needed in cleaning contaminated surfaces especially if they are wood or other combustible material.

Liquids

If the liquid is volatile and flammable, all flames should be extinguished and adequate ventilation ensured.

Water-soluble liquids may be diluted and mopped up using absorbent paper, cloths or a mop and bucket. Special care is required with corrosive liquids and strong oxidising agents. Concentrated acids should be diluted and then liberally sprinkled with sodium carbonate (soda ash is a cheap, commercial form) before swabbing down the area with a large volume of water. All contaminated cloths and mops must be thoroughly washed.

The method chosen to deal with spills of **concentrated sulphuric acid** should depend on the quantity of acid spilt. Small quantities on the skin should be flooded with water. If there is insufficient water available the excess acid should be mopped up first with a dry cloth or absorbent paper.

Water-immiscible liquids may be treated with sand or mineral absorbent (eg cat litter) to prevent spreading, followed by scraping and mopping into a suitable container prior to removal for disposal. Only very small bench spills may be treated by swabbing into a sink followed by flushing with large volumes of water. A dispersing agent such as "Teepol" may be useful when swabbing down.

Mercury may be recovered mechanically (eg using a teat pipette). Small drops may be collected by treating the affected area with a paste of copper powder and dilute sulphuric acid or with a slurry of calcium hydroxide and flowers of sulphur in hot water, the resulting mixture being swept up after 24 hours. A dry mixture of calcium hydroxide and flowers of sulphur should be swept into any cracks in benches or floor to reduce the rate of evaporation of very small quantities of hidden trapped mercury.

Gases

The room ventilation should be increased to try to ensure that the gases are swept into the outside air and not allowed to contaminate corridors.

15.10   Disposal of Chemicals

The disposal of even small quantities of chemicals requires a great deal of thought.

Topics Ch.13
Hazcards

Small quantities of most chemicals may be washed down the sink with a very large excess of water or flushed down the toilet. Phosphorus (red or white), alkali metals and small volumes of flammable liquids (less than 500 cm^3) may be burnt on open ground and the residue dug in provided the burning does not present a hazard, eg toxic gases produced. Highly volatile liquids in small quantities may be left in a safe place to evaporate. For large quantities of chemicals, or those which present particular difficulty, seek advice from CLEAPSS, SSERC [see 1.2], or the local waste disposal authority.

The problem is greater if the identity of containers is unknown. It is necessary to comply with the *Environmental Protection Act* Sections 33 and 34.

16 Storage of Chemicals

16.1 General Considerations

Chemical stores should be conveniently situated and organised to facilitate the location and retrieval of chemicals and yet be secure against the entry of unauthorised persons. If they are not convenient, human nature is such that they will not be used and this may lead to the unofficial use of other odd cupboards. These may be unsuitable and, being unplanned, possibly dangerous. Stores must also be safe to work in, easy to escape from in the event of a disaster and should not present a risk to others, ie the rest of the school population or to the public at large.

> A store and its system of use may offer sufficient security to prevent unauthorised access and possible theft of chemicals. If it does not, then some of the more toxic and hazardous substances may need to be locked up in cupboards within the store.

The slow turnover of chemicals in schools can give rise to problems not faced by other sectors of industry.

Teachers should resist the temptation to purchase more than is needed for, say, two year's supply, except in those cases where the materials have an indefinite shelf life.

DfEE Safety
Ch. 9.3

Handbook
Ch. 7

Haz Man

Topics Ch. 8

Certain chemicals are better bought fresh every year and the stock of flammable liquids should not exceed that necessary for one and a half year's use. If possible arrange to have the year's requisition of flammables delivered in three termly batches. Any stock which shows signs of deterioration, eg potassium with a yellow surface, should be disposed of [see 15.7]. Many have a short shelf life, eg ethoxyethane, and should be disposed of at the end of that stipulated life.

All chemicals should be date stamped on arrival in school. A record of the chemical stock should be maintained, showing the storage location for each chemical and this list should be checked annually. Such a system assists in the locating and the re-ordering of chemicals. There are advantages in using a computer database. Records are also of great value in the event of a fire or a theft of chemicals from the school.

All reagent bottles and containers for use in the laboratory should be of a size that can be safely held by the smallest hand that uses them. Care is needed when chemicals are transported between stores and preparation rooms to laboratories. Bottles should not be carried by the neck; special bottle carriers are recommended and it is best to avoid busy times between periods when classes are moving about. Boxes and trolleys should be fitted with some simple form of packing to prevent reagent bottles falling over. A sheet of synthetic foam with holes cut out for containers and bottles is one possibility.

All containers should be clearly labelled at all times. Chemicals kept in corrosive atmospheres or in outside stores where the labels often deteriorate can be identified by using plastic tags tied round the neck of the bottle or jar.

> Periodic checks should be made of labels especially in those situations above where the labels can rapidly decay. There is advantage in writing directly onto plastic bottles which have a tendency to shed their labels.
>
> Chemicals which can deteriorate slowly with evolution of gas, eg hydrogen peroxide, should be kept in a cool place and the bottle cap should be of the vented type. Those whose decomposition is accelerated by light should be stored in dark bottles. Bottles of chemicals which are hydrolysed by the moisture of the air, eg calcium dicarbide or calcium phosphide, can have their original stoppers replaced by rubber bungs.
>
> In cases where the chemical attacks the bung, eg silicon tetrachloride or bromine, proprietary PTFE sleeves designed for ground glass joints of the same size can be fitted to the glass stopper. A better, though more expensive option, is to purchase PTFE stoppers for these few bottles. Small quantities of these chemicals can be kept in a desiccator over anhydrous calcium chloride. Some schools' suppliers now sell these chemicals in small quantities.
>
> Spill kits should be available [see 15.9] and certain chemicals should have their own special spill treatment materials stored beside the container, eg sodium carbonate or sodium thiosulphate for neutralising bromine.

Topics Ch.11

Handbook Ch. 7.7

Haz Man

16.2 Location and Design of Stores

There are legal requirements to store and handle chemicals safely. The *HSW Act* [see Ch.2] places a general duty on employers to ensure there is an absence of risk to the health and safety, both of their employees and of others, which may result from the keeping, handling and use of dangerous substances. This duty is further amplified by the *Management Regulations* [see Ch.3] and the *COSHH Regulations*, which require the employer to make a suitable and sufficient assessment of the risks to health and safety [see 3.2 and 3.4].

The *COSHH Regulations* focus on the risks resulting from the use of substances hazardous to health and, where necessary, require either the removal of the offending chemical or the use of adequate control measures to reduce the risks. An example would be where the concentration of various vapours in the atmosphere of a store exceeded the OES or MEL [see 15.3] of the chemicals concerned; fitting the caps on the containers more tightly and improving the ventilation would probably be all that was needed. Equally the separation of bottles of incompatible chemicals which, if accidentally mixed would react to produce a toxic gas, would also be seen as a control measure. It should be stressed that it is for each employer, who has the responsibility to consider appropriate storage arrangements, to ensure that risks to the health of those using the store are sufficiently low. Employees, ie teachers and technicians, have a duty to follow the procedures laid down by their employer and to report any observable deficiencies in the system.

There are many ways of providing storage and there is no set arrangement which can be a model for all schools. An arrangement which works well in one school may be downright dangerous in another, possibly on account of a different geography. It is not necessary to have an outside store and there are several advantages in having a store within the building, for example convenience and ease of access or the avoidance of long carries, especially in bad weather with the added danger of slipping. Storage of flammables will have to be approved by the local fire prevention officer and an internal store will have to have a fire resistance of at least half an hour. Preparation rooms may be used for some storage provided that:

(i)   more care is taken with security and
(ii) the safety and health of those working in the room are not compromised since they will spend much of their working day close to stored chemicals.

Ventilation will be more important and certain chemicals should be taken to the fume cupboard in an adjoining laboratory for decanting or dispensing from larger bottles.

The door of the chemical store should open outwards and be fitted with a yale type of lock which can always be opened from the inside without the need of a key. Flammables should be stored at the furthest point from the door. Stores need adequate ventilation, preferably at both high and low levels. If natural ventilation is inadequate some form of forced ventilation will be needed. The motors on such fans will need to be spark-proof. If some heating is needed to prevent condensation, it should also be spark-proof and flame-free. Where flammables are not dispensed or decanted there is no need for special spark-proof lighting fixtures and switches [see 11.4].

Topics.
Ch.10

Shelving should be robust and firmly fixed to prevent movement and should be regularly inspected for signs of corrosion or weakening. Some find a lip fitted to the edge of the shelf helpful in keeping bottles from falling from the shelf, but then extra care is needed when lifting bottles from that shelf. Ideally shelves should be of single-container width as this greatly facilitates locating and retrieving chemicals and greatly assists stocktaking, thus ensuring that accidental over-ordering does not occur. It is useful to store some bottles in trays which have sufficient capacity to contain a spill resulting from the breakage of several of the bottles.

The storage of highly flammable liquids presents problems because of conflicting statutory requirements.

In industry storage of flammables is governed by the *Highly Flammable Liquids and Liquefied Petroleum Gases Regulations* and, although strictly not applying to schools, the requirements of these Regulations are used by the Health and Safety Executive as a guide to good practice. The HSE has further interpreted certain aspects of the Regulations in its guidance note *HS(G) 51. The storage of flammable liquids in containers*. These Regulations define a highly flammable liquid as one with a flash point of less than 32 °C and permit bottles of capacity of less than 500 cm^3 to be kept on the open shelf and up to 50 litres in a fire-resistant cupboard in a preparation room or store; still larger quantities may be kept in a store or bin separate from the "workroom". 50 litres should cover all the requirements of most science departments. In all matters concerning the arrangements for the storage of flammables the local fire prevention officer must be consulted. As they have considerable powers of discretion, local practice may vary considerably, even within the boundaries of one education authority. Note that the *CHIP Regulations*, which are concerned with the labelling and transport of chemicals, use slightly different definitions of flammability [see 15.2].

As a reasonable compromise, it is suggested that schools should store as flammables in the fire resistant cabinet:

(i) **liquids with a flash point equal to or less than 32** °C. Some flash points are listed in Table 15.3 [section 15.6]. Others can be obtained from entries in catalogues, the label on the bottle, or from the supplier's Safety Data Sheets (MSDS). Liquids with flash points less than 21 °C will be easily recognised by the flame hazard pictogram [see 7.9] on the container.

(ii) **other flammable liquids with a flash point greater than 32** °C and up to 55 °C as far as space permits, especially any with flash points in the mid-thirties, eg pentanol.

16.3 Special Cases

Chemicals should not be stored in adjacent positions if there is a danger of a violent reaction or of a reaction producing a toxic gas in the event of accidental contact following breakage.

There is a need to separate certain classes of chemicals which present special problems (see below). A label placed at what would be the expected position in any system used for the bulk of the chemicals, for example, one based on either an alphabetical system or on a classification by families, can re-direct the person to the new location. This might be in another store or in separate cupboards, boxes or bins in the same storeroom.

Toxic chemicals and other highly hazardous chemicals will have to be locked inside a cupboard if the storeroom itself is not kept locked all the time. A guide to the toxicity may be obtained from the hazard warning on the label or from the supplier's catalogue.

Placing together chemicals, simply because they are all toxic, can unwittingly create a very dangerous situation, with oxidising agents, reducing agents and flammables in close proximity. This is why the secure storeroom referred to in 16.1 is to be preferred to the old concept of a poisons cupboard.

Radioactive sources and substances must be kept in one or more locked and marked cupboards located at least 3 m, and preferably further away, from permanently occupied areas [see 12.8].[1] They should not be kept in the same room as the flammable store and, if at all possible, not in the chemical store.

Concentrated acids and alkalies. Stock bottles should be located just above floor level, with a means of limiting spills. This could be achieved by having trays filled with absorbent placed underneath the bottom shelf.

Highly flammable liquids and refrigerators. Only refrigerators specially designed or modified with spark-proof contacts on the internal light switch and thermostat should be used for storing flammable liquids [see 15.6]. Otherwise the door should carry a large permanent notice stating that the refrigerator is unsuitable for storage of flammables.

Other flammable substances such as the water-reactives like **sodium, potassium or alkali metal hydrides** should be stored separately from flammable solvents. The quantities held are usually small and a metal tin would be suitable. **Phosphorus** should be kept separate from both the flammable solvents and from the alkali metals. It is probably not necessary to keep phosphorus in an outside store, but if it is, care must be taken to ensure that the water in the bottle neither freezes, nor evaporates. (Sodium chloride solution is less likely to do either).

Substances with two characteristics which may not be stored in either category. Examples are alkyl nitrites or organic peroxides which are both highly flammable and oxidising. They must not be stored with flammables nor with oxidising agents.

Volatile and hydrolysable substances such as **bromine, silicon tetrachloride, anhydrous aluminium chloride** and **acid chlorides** should, if possible, be kept in a separate store. It is particularly important that they are kept away from stocks of sodium and other active metals. Storage of other hydrolysable chemicals in fume cupboards is not recommended unless that cupboard is used solely for this purpose and is operating either continuously or intermittently with the aid of a time switch.

Some schools may still possess 500 g aluminium canisters of liquid sulphur dioxide. The valves on these are prone to corroding and seizing up if kept near volatile corrosives or in a fume cupboard. These canisters are best

---

[1] *Administrative Memorandum AM 1/92*, DfE & WO;
   SOED *Circular 1166* and *Explanatory Notes*;
   DENI *The Use of Ionising Radiations in Educational Establishments*, 1986

stored on open shelves in a well-ventilated room. Alternatively they can be placed inside a plastic bag with some desiccant. Tubing should not be left connected to the valve during storage.

Handbook
Ch. 13.3

Haz Man

Compressed gases: cylinders should be kept in an upright position, either clamped to a fixture or chained to a trolley. Their place of storage should be cool, ventilated and not near flammables [see 9.1].[2]

---

[2] See *Educ. Sci.*, Sept 1980

17 First Aid and Emergency Treatment

17.1 Being Prepared for Accidents

However safe and well organised a science department may be, there is always a real possibility of accidents and the department must be prepared for this. In particular, there may be the need for what most people would call "first aid". Strictly speaking, the term "first aid" should be reserved for the treatment of casualties by those who have followed an approved training course as a first aider, and who have a valid, up to date certificate. It is unwise for those who have NOT had formal training to attempt first aid. However, in the case of certain accidents which might arise in a school laboratory it is essential to take immediate remedial measures [see 17.2] before a trained first aider arrives, or where one is not available. In the latter case, there must be an "Appointed Person" whose job it is to take charge, call an ambulance if necessary and apply immediate remedial measures.

Under the *First Aid Regulations* employers must ensure that there is adequate and appropriate provision for first aid. This includes ensuring that there is an adequate number of appropriately trained first aiders. Although it might be thought desirable, there is no statutory requirement for science staff to be trained as first aiders. The *Approved Code of Practice* and its associated *Guidance* suggest that first aid kits must be accessible and that there may be a need for first aid provision in different parts of an establishment, particularly where there are self-contained working areas. There is no statutory requirement to have a first aid kit or box in every laboratory, or even in every preparation room, although the Education Service Advisory Committee did endorse[1] an earlier DES recommendation that there should be a kit in every laboratory. However, this has been somewhat overtaken by recent developments in first aid training, and trained first aiders now may well bring their own kit with them. Nevertheless, first aid kits must be easily accessible throughout the science

---

[1] *First Aid in Educational Establishments*, Health and Safety Commission, 1985, ISBN 0 1188 387377

department. Exactly where and how many will depend on the size and geography of the department: an isolated laboratory may well need its own kit. Common sense should prevail.

The *Approved Code of Practice* and its associated *Guidance* state that first aid kits should contain only items shown in Table 17.1.

Table 17.1

APPROVED CONTENTS OF FIRST AID KITS

A card giving general first aid guidance
20 individually wrapped, sterile, adhesive dressings
6 individually wrapped triangular bandages (preferably sterile)
6 safety pins
6 medium-sized (10 cm × 8 cm), individually wrapped, sterile, unmedicated, wound dressings
2 large (13 cm × 9 cm), individually wrapped, sterile, unmedicated, wound dressings
3 extra large (28 cm × 18 cm), individually wrapped, sterile, unmedicated, wound dressings
2 sterile eye pads

In view of the health risks from AIDS and hepatitis the following are sensible additions to the Approved List:

- disposable gloves, for use when dealing with blood and other body fluids
- Vent-Aid, or similar disposable face shield

Staff responsible for first aid should check the contents of all boxes to ensure that adequate supplies of each item are available and that nothing else is kept there. The boxes should be kept clean and dry, and should be clearly marked with a white cross on a green background.

In the past various antidotes have been suggested for use when chemicals have been swallowed or splashed onto the skin. Most of these (including the use of burn creams) are now considered to do more harm than good.

Science staff cannot expect trained first aiders to be scientifically knowledgeable. Thus, for example, they may be confused about the difference between acids and alkalies. It may be necessary, particularly in the case of alkali in the eye, to impress on the first aider the necessity for irrigation of the eye to continue even during the journey to hospital. An explanatory note should accompany any patient sent for treatment so that ambiguities do not arise.

Under *RIDDOR* (the *Reporting of Injuries, Diseases and Dangerous Occurrences Regulations*), all major injuries (as defined in the Regulations) must be reported to the Health and Safety Executive immediately by telephone. This includes injury requiring medical treatment due to electric shock. In addition, education authorities and/or school governors will usually require records to be kept of all accidents which a trained first aider has attended. Science staff must comply with whatever record-keeping system is required by their employer [see 2.4].

17.2 Immediate Remedial Measures

In some accidents in science laboratories, seconds count. Serious injury may be avoided if those present take Immediate Remedial Measures in the minute or two before the trained first aider arrives. The list in Table 17.2 gives appropriate guidance on what it is reasonable to expect science teachers and technicians to do in such situations. It may be freely copied by purchasing institutions and it would be sensible to post copies on the walls of all laboratories and preparation rooms. The table might also be given to pupils in appropriate circumstances.

Staff should be given regular training in these techniques. Except for resuscitation, where a first aider should provide the training, training in most of these techniques can be led by an experienced science teacher or technician as a part of a departmental meeting. Such training should be repeated from time to time.

Some children may have special medical needs, eg haemophiliacs. There should be a clear whole-school policy on dealing with accidents to such children. Staff must know who they are and what the agreed procedures are.

17.3 First Aid

This section gives explanations of, or more details about, some of the procedures listed in the Immediate Remedial Measures [see 17.2]. It also gives some details about first aid procedures which may be useful if no trained first aider is available, eg in remote areas outside the UK. These are no substitute for proper first aid and medical treatment. See recognised first aid handbooks.[2]

> The aim of laboratory first aid is to minimise the immediate effects of an accident on a person. The extent of treatment will depend on a number of factors, not the least being the estimated delay before professional attention can be given. All first aid procedures must comply with any local regulations. Medical aid must be obtained in every case of serious injury, in all cases of injury to the eye and whenever in doubt. The nature of the accident should be explained when seeking aid.

---

[2] *First Aid Manual*: the authorised manual of the St John Ambulance, St Andrews Ambulance Association and the British Red Cross, 6th edition, 1992 (reprinted 1994)

Table 17.2

IMMEDIATE REMEDIAL MEASURES

What Science Staff should do while waiting for a First Aider

Chemical splashes in the eye
Immediately wash the eye with running water for at least 10 minutes, *and for much longer in the case of alkalies.* The flow should be slow and the eyelids should be held back. Afterwards the casualty should be taken to hospital (and, for alkalies, irrigation continued during the journey).

Chemical splashes on the skin
Wash the skin for 5 minutes or until all traces of the chemical have disappeared. Remove clothing as necessary. If the chemical adheres to the skin, wash gently with soap.

Chemicals in the mouth, perhaps swallowed
Do no more than wash out the casualty's mouth. Do *NOT* induce vomiting. After any treatment by the first aider, the casualty should be taken to hospital.

Burns
Cool under gently running water until first aid arrives.

Toxic gas
Sit the casualty down in fresh air.

Hair on fire
Smother with a cloth.

Clothing on fire
Smother by laying the casualty on the ground, flames on top. Spread a thick cloth or garment on top if necessary. A fire blanket is ideal but use only if very close by.

Electric shock
Taking care for your own safety, break contact by switching off or pulling out the plug. If it is necessary to move the casualty clear, use a broom handle or wooden window pole or wear rubber gloves. If casualty is unconscious, check that airways are clear and that the casualty is breathing and has a pulse. If so, place casualty in recovery position. If the casualty is not breathing but has a pulse artificial ventilation is essential. If there is no breathing or pulse, call an ambulance and begin Cardio-Pulmonary Resuscitation.

Severe cuts
Lower the casualty to the floor and raise the wound as high as possible. Get the casualty to apply pressure on or as close to the cut as possible, using fingers, a pad of cloth, or, better, a sterile dressing. If the casualty is unable to do so, apply pressure yourself, but protect yourself from contamination by blood if at all possible. Leave any embedded large bodies and press around them.

Asthma attack
Asthmatic pupils will have been trained in what to do. Allow them access to their medication, and permit them to take the appropriate steps.

Eye Accidents

While taking immediate remedial measures make sure that medical aid is sent for in all but the most trivial accidents to the eye. This includes those caused by glass, alkali metals, bromine (see below), phosphorus, or by solutions of acids, alkalies or other corrosives unless extremely dilute. Send the person for medical treatment in all other cases if, after taking immediate remedial measures, irritation, discomfort or impairment of sight continues.

Chemicals in the eye

As quickly as possible flood the eye thoroughly with a large quantity of gently running water, ensuring that the water bathes the eyeball by gently prising open the eyelids. Ensure that the chemical is not washed into the other eye, or onto the rest of the face. Continue irrigation for at least 10 minutes.

If there is a possibility that **alkali** may have entered the eye, continue irrigation indefinitely, even during the journey to hospital. First aiders and ambulance crew should be told that this is necessary.

Because of the difficulty of keeping the contents clean, eyewash bottles should be used only if freshly filled with tap water. Sealed sterile wash bottles are available, but are expensive, and contain an inadequate quantity of water (unless several bottles are used, further increasing costs).

After flooding with water for at least 10 minutes, a sterile eye pad should be applied before sending the person for medical treatment.

Inert solids in the eye (eg, glass)

Do not attempt to remove glass etc. Stop the casualty rubbing or touching the eye and keep the person as still as possible.

If chemical contamination has also occurred, gently flood the eye with water ensuring that this bathes the eyeball and removes as much of the contamination as possible without initiating further damage to the eye. Sterile eye pads should be applied to **both** eyes to keep eye movement to a minimum.

Burns and Scalds

Reduce pain by cooling the burn by immersion in cold water or under running cold water for at least ten minutes. Do not attempt to remove clothing if it is sticking to the skin, but **do** remove watches or items of jewellery as the affected area will swell. Cover loosely with a dry sterile triangular bandage. (Plastic kitchen film or even a clean plastic bag can be used if the bandage is not available). In the case of serious burns (larger in area than 6 cm^2, ie a fifty pence coin), the casualty should be sent to hospital for treatment.

Burns, whether serious or not, should **never** be treated with tannic acid, oil, cream or antiseptic ointment.

Chemical Burns

Some chemicals in contact with the skin will cause burns. In general, treat as for heat burns.

Treat splashes of hazardous chemicals on the skin as follows.

- Flood the surface with large quantities of running water for several minutes until satisfied that the chemical has been removed.
- Remove all contaminated clothing, cutting when necessary and taking care not to contaminate yourself in the process.
- Cover the area with a dry sterile triangular bandage (a **wet** bandage in the case of **phosphorus** burns) and consider elevating a burnt hand or arm if this makes the casualty more comfortable.
- Obtain immediate medical treatment for serious burns and all those involving contact with alkali metals, bromine, phenol or phosphorus.

Bromine burns are very serious and heal only with difficulty. Whenever bromine is being used, the risk assessment should require a 20% (1 M) solution of sodium thiosulphate to be at hand and immediately applied if contamination occurs, **before** following the procedure above. **If it is not immediately available do not waste time** searching for sodium thiosulphate: flood with water instead.

Cuts

Where possible get the casualty to carry out her or his own treatment, to minimise the risk of contact with blood and hence the possible transmission of hepatitis or HIV. Alternatively wear disposable surgical gloves to protect yourself; trained first aiders will often bring their own gloves.

Get the casualty to apply pressure on or as close to the cut as possible, using fingers, a pad of cloth, or, better, a sterile dressing. If the casualty is unable to do so, apply pressure yourself.

Minor cuts and puncture wounds
Any dirt and small pieces of glass should be removed, by the casualty if possible, the wound washed under running water and dried carefully with a paper towel or tissue. The casualty should apply a clean sterile dressing.

Wounds with glass (or metal) embedded
Should a large piece of glass (eg, tubing or rod) or metal (eg, wire) be embedded, it may be best to leave this in place, since its removal may seriously increase bleeding. The affected limb should be elevated and the casualty laid down if possible. The wound should be protected with a sterile pad to prevent the movement of the embedded article and covered with a bandage. A hand or arm should be supported in a sling, if possible. Immediate medical aid should be obtained.

Arterial bleeding
The casualty should be laid down and the limb raised. If possible, the casualty should apply pressure over the wound with a thick, dry, sterile

pad. If this pad becomes soaked through with blood, it should **not** be removed but another large pad placed on top and the pressure maintained by a firm bandage. An ambulance should be called as soon as possible after starting first aid, preferably by getting someone other than the first aider to do so.

Toxic solids or liquids in the mouth or swallowed

The casualty should spit out immediately and wash her or his mouth with much water. **Do NOT induce vomiting.** An ambulance should be called. Clothing around the neck should be loosened: there may be a rapid internal swelling of the airway.

- **Alkalies or acids** (including ethanedioic (oxalic) acid). If medical treatment is delayed, a lot of cold water should be given in small sips.
- The use of emetics can be dangerous and cause complications: they should only be used if qualified medical attention is not readily available. If the school is in a remote area, information should be sought in advance for the most suitable procedure to be followed in such an eventuality.

Inhalation of gases or vapours

The person should be removed to an uncontaminated room (but **not** out of doors, as a sudden temperature change may cause further problems for asthmatics), after first ensuring your own safety. Clothing should be loosened, and the casualty treated as for shock (see below). If breathing has stopped but there is still a pulse, artificial ventilation may be applied (see below), while sending for an ambulance.

Do **NOT** attempt to apply any antidote, as there is a risk it could make the problem worse. If the dose is more than very trivial, s/he should be kept warm and still and medical aid summoned urgently.

Shock

All accidents produce some shock. The shocked person should be made to lie down, with feet raised slightly, and kept warm. Even for mild shock, it is now considered unwise to give drinks of tea or coffee. Liquids must never be given to an unconscious person.

The unconscious
The casualty should be placed in the recovery position (Figure 17.1) so that any liquid can drain out of the mouth. Any dentures should be removed only if they are damaged or disturbed.
    If breathing has stopped, artificial ventilation should be given (see p. 110).

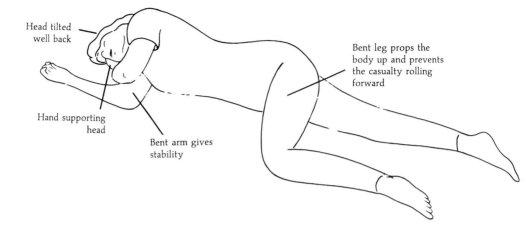

Head tilted
well back

Bent leg props the
body up and prevents
the casualty rolling
forward

Hand supporting
head

Bent arm gives
stability

Figure 17.1

Electric shock

First the supply should be switched off, then the casualty treated for shock as above.

> If it is impossible to switch off immediately, the casualty should be dragged away, using dry clothes or other insulating material while standing on an insulating material.
>
> Having given artificial ventilation if breathing has stopped, it may be necessary then to treat burns (see above). Electricity may produce deep-seated burns and there may be little or no feeling as the nerves are damaged.

Resuscitation

A casualty who is unconscious, has a pulse but is not breathing will require artificial ventilation (see below) to maintain the supply of oxygenated blood via the heart to the brain.

A casualty who is unconscious, is not breathing and has no pulse (cardiac arrest) will require artificial ventilation **and** chest compression to force the oxygenated blood through the heart to the brain. This is called cardio-pulmonary resuscitation or CPR (see below).

Artificial ventilation

Artificial ventilation is the essential treatment required by the victim of any accident which restricts the amount of oxygen available to the body or causes breathing to stop. The treatment must be given without delay or the central nervous system suffers damage from which it cannot recover and the heart ceases to beat.

> The Expired Air Method (mouth-to-mouth or mouth-to-nose) is the most effective method and is briefly described here. This description is not a

substitute for proper instruction in the method, and as many people as possible should obtain instruction from one of the recognised first aid organisations, or via a course organised by their employer.

To carry out Mouth-to-Mouth Ventilation
This method is appropriate for a casualty who is unconscious, and not breathing, but who has a pulse

(a)   Place the patient on his/her back.
(b)   Quickly inspect the mouth and nose to make sure they are free from obvious obstruction, eg displaced or broken false teeth.
(c)   Tilt the patient's head fully back to give a clear airway (Figure 17. 2).

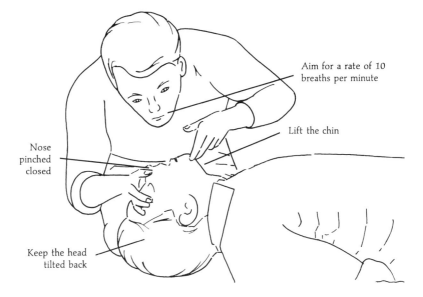

Aim for a rate of 10 breaths per minute

Lift the chin

Nose pinched closed

Keep the head tilted back

Figure 17.2

(d)   Breathe in, open your mouth wide and make an airtight seal over the nose (or mouth) of the patient and blow gently. If your mouth is over the nose, see that the patient's lips are closed, and if over the mouth, seal the patient's nose with your cheek, or by pinching the nostrils.
(e)   After blowing, turn your head to watch for chest movement, and inhale in readiness to blow again.
(f)   If the patient's chest does not rise, check that the mouth and throat are clear of obstruction and that the head is tilted backwards as far as possible. Clearing an obstruction may require back slaps, or failing this abdominal thrusts [Figure 17.3].
(g)   Commence with ten breaths of mouth-to-mouth ventilation per minute. Call an ambulance, or, better still, send someone else to call one. Continue with ventilation until help arrives.
(h)   In the unlikely event of small children and babies needing ventilation in the laboratory, inflation at the rate of about twenty a minute is achieved by a series of puffs, each one ceasing as the chest starts to rise. In no circumstances should air be blown violently into a baby's lungs.

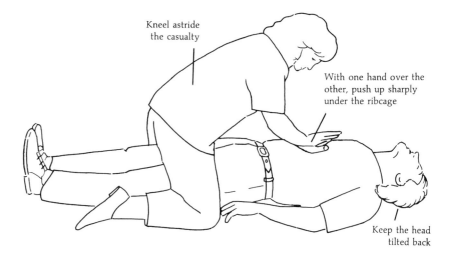

Kneel astride
the casualty

With one hand over the
other, push up sharply
under the ribcage

Keep the head
tilted back

Figure 17.3

Cardio-pulmonary resuscitation (CPR)

The chance that CPR will, by itself, re-start a heart that has stopped is remote. Specialised treatment and defibrillation is almost always necessary. If the casualty is to have any chance of survival once CPR is started it must be continued until professional help arrives. Only a brief outline of CPR is given here since it should be attempted by an untrained person only in an extreme emergency and then only after expert help has been called for.

To carry out CPR
This method is appropriate for a casualty who is unconscious, **not** breathing and who has **no** pulse.

(a) Call an ambulance.
(b) Give two breaths of artificial ventilation (see above).
(c) Give 15 chest compressions (see below).
(d) Give two more ventilations, then 15 further compressions and continue this sequence until expert help arrives.
(e) Do not interrupt CPR to check for a pulse unless there is evidence of returning circulation.
(f) In the unlikely event of small children and babies needing CPR in the laboratory, a reduced level of chest compression is required, 2-3 cm, but at a more rapid rate, 100 per minute, the sequence being five compressions to each ventilation.

Chest Compression as part of CPR
(a) Place the casualty flat on her / his back on a firm surface. Kneel down and slide the middle and index fingers of one hand up the centre line of the rib cage and locate the point where the ribs join. Place your middle finger at this point and your index finger on the breastbone above (Figure 17.4).

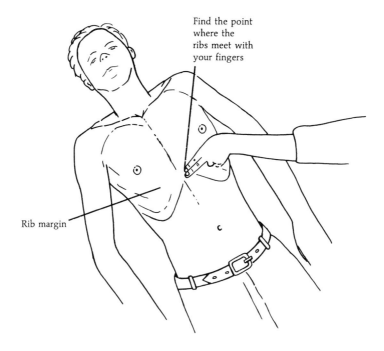

Find the point
where the
ribs meet with
your fingers

Rib margin

Figure 17.4

(b) Slide the heel of the other hand down the breastbone until it reaches
your index finger. This is where compression is needed (Figure 17.5).

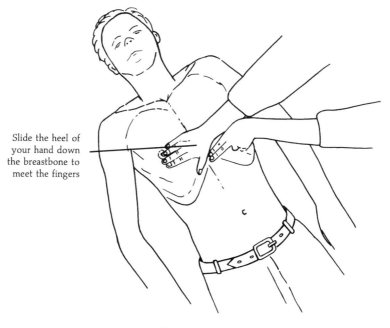

Slide the heel of
your hand down
the breastbone to
meet the fingers

Figure 17.5

(c) Place the heel of your first hand on top of the other and interlock the fingers, keeping them up and away from the ribs (Figure 17.6).

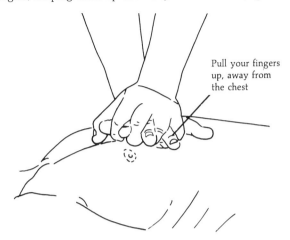

Pull your fingers up, away from the chest

Figure 17.6

(d) Lean well over the casualty and with the arms straight press down vertically on the breast bone to depress it 4-5 cm. Release the pressure but keeps hands in place (Figure 17.7).

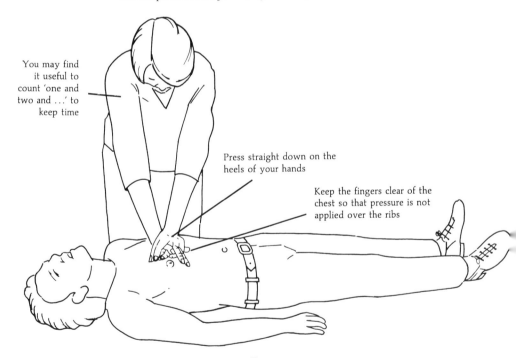

You may find it useful to count 'one and two and ...' to keep time

Press straight down on the heels of your hands

Keep the fingers clear of the chest so that pressure is not applied over the ribs

Figure 17.7

(e) Repeat at a rate of about 80 compressions per minute but combine with ventilation in the ratio of 15:2, as described above.

Index